READ ME FIRST

Younger Poems
for Every Day of the Year

Key Stages 1 and 2

Chosen by Louise Bolongaro

Illustrated by Georgie Ripper

MACMILLAN CHILDREN'S BOOKS

First published 2003
by Macmillan Children's Books
a division of Macmillan Publishers Limited
20 New Wharf Road, London N1 9RR
Basingstoke and Oxford
www.panmacmillan.com

Associated companies throughout the world

ISBN 0 330 41343 0

1 3 5 7 9 8 6 4 2

A CIP catalogue record for this book is available from the British Library.

Printed by Mackays of Chatham plc, Chatham, Kent.

Contents

JANUARY

Contents

Contents

MARCH

Contents

Contents

Contents

Contents

JUNE

Contents

Contents

Contents

Contents

Contents

Contents

Contents

Contents

DECEMBER

Contents

January

1st

New Day

The day is so new
You can hear it yawning,
Listen:

The new day
is yawning
and stretching

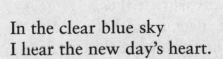

and waiting to start.

In the clear blue sky
I hear the new day's heart.

Ian McMillan

2nd

They Never Send Sam to the Store Anymore

The day they sent Sam to the grocery store
to purchase a carton of eggs,
he brought back a pear with a pearl in its core,
and a leopard with lavender legs.

He returned with an elephant small as a mouse,
a baseball that bounces a mile,
a little tame dragon that heats up the house,
and a lantern that lights when they smile.

Sam brought them a snowball that never feels cold,
a gossamer carpet that flies,
a salmon of silver, a grackel of gold,
and an ermine with emerald eyes.

They never send Sam to the store anymore,
no matter how often he begs,
for he brought back a dodo that danced on the
    floor,
But he didn't bring home any eggs.

Jack Prelutsky

You and I Shall Go

It is above that you and I shall go;
Along the Milky Way you and I shall go;
Along the flower trail you and I shall go;
Picking flowers on our way you and I shall go.

Wintu

The Spangled Pandemonium

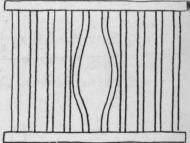

The spangled pandemonium
Is missing from the zoo.
He bent the bars the barest bit,
And slithered glibly through.

He crawled across the moated wall,
He climbed the mango tree,
And when the keeper scrambled up,
He nipped him in the knee.

To all of you, a warning
Not to wander after dark,
Or if you must, make very sure
You stay out of the park.

For the spangled pandemonium
Is missing from the zoo,
And since he nipped his keeper,
He would just as soon nip you.

Palmer Brown

Poor Crow!

Give me something to eat,
   Good people, I pray;
I have really not had
   One mouthful today!

I am hungry and cold,
   And last night I dreamed
A scarecrow had caught me—
   Good Lord, how I screamed!

Of one little children
    And six ailing wives
(No, one wife and six children),
    Not one of them thrives.

So pity my case,
    Dear people, I pray;
I'm honest, and really
    I've come a long way.

Mary Mapes Dodge

Sensible Questions

"Suppose the land turned into the sea?"
"Don't be stupid! It couldn't be!"

"Suppose the sea turned into the land?"
"It wouldn't happen. You don't understand!"

"Suppose I waved this grassy stalk,
And Max the dog began to talk?"

"Your fancy's foolish. Your ways are wild!
I often think you're a silly child!"

But Marigold waved her stalk of grass
And all she had asked about came to pass.

The land rolled up and the sea rolled over
The waves were covered with grass and clover,

While Marigold and her reproving aunt
Who'd kept on saying "Don't!" and "Can't",

Were up to their necks in a wild green sea –
And Max the dog said, "Fiddle dee dee!"

Margaret Mahy

7th

Polar Bear

The secret of the polar bear
Is that he wears long underwear.

Gail Kredenser

Time to Get Up

A birdie with a yellow bill
Hopped upon the window sill,
Cocked his shining eye and said:
"'Aint you 'shamed, you sleepy-head?"

Robert Louis Stevenson

9th

Bedbugs' Marching Song

Bedbugs
Have the right
To bite.

Bedbugs
Of the world
Unite.

Don't let
These humans
Sleep too tight.

John Agard

Waking Up

Oh! I have just had such a lovely dream!
And then I woke,
And all the dream went out like kettle-steam,
Or chimney-smoke.

My dream was all about – how funny, though!
I've only just
Dreamed it, and now it has begun to blow
Away like dust.

In it I went – no! in my dream I had –
No, that's not it!
I can't remember, oh, it is *too* bad,
My dream a bit.

But I saw something beautiful, I'm sure –
Then someone spoke,
And then I didn't see it any more,
Because I woke.

Eleanor Farjeon

11th

Rain

There are holes in the sky
Where the rain gets in,
But they're ever so small
That's why rain is thin.

Spike Milligan

Zebra

A zebra lies upon the road
And we walk all over him smartly.
He gets a pain, right on his vein.
Just think of this when you cross the road
And step on his stripes, whole or partly.

Jon Burnby, age 8

Two Little Dogs

Two little dogs
Sat by the fire
Over a fender of coal-dust;
Said one little dog
To the other little dog,
If you don't talk, why, I must.

Anon.

14th

I've Got a Dog

I've got a dog as thin as a rail,
He's got fleas all over his tail;
Every time his tail goes flop,
The fleas on the bottom all hop to the top.

Anon.

15th

The Bottle of Perfume

The bottle of perfume that Willie sent
Was highly displeasing to Millicent.
Her thanks were so cold,
They quarrelled, I'm told,
Through that silly scent Willie sent Millicent.

Anon.

16th

Mad Hatter's Song

Twinkle, twinkle, little bat!
How I wonder what you're at!
Up above the world you fly,
Like a tea-tray in the sky.
Twinkle, twinkle –

Lewis Carroll

New Sights

I like to see a thing I know
Has not been seen before,
That's why I cut my apple through
To look into the core.

It's nice to think, though many an eye
Has seen the ruddy skin,
Mine is the very first to spy
The five brown pips within.

Anon.

The Hippopotamus's Birthday

He has opened all his parcels
 but the largest and the last;
His hopes are at their highest
 and his heart is beating fast.
O happy Hippopotamus,
 what lovely gift is here?
He cuts the string. The world stands still.
 A pair of boots appear!

O little Hippopotamus,
   the sorrows of the small!
He dropped two tears to mingle
   with the flowing Senegal;
And the "Thank you" that he uttered
   was the saddest ever heard
In the Senegambian jungle
   from the mouth of beast or bird.

E. V. Rieu

Jungle Wedding

When the hairy hippopotamus
And dapper duck-billed playtpus
Decided to get married in the spring,
All the jungle bells were ringing

And the tree-top choirs were singing,
But they couldn't find a shop to buy a ring.

Clive Webster

Baby Orang-utan

Bold flare of orange –
a struck match
against his mother's breast

he listens to her heartbeat
going *yes yes yes*

Helen Dunmore

Bedtime

Five minutes, five minutes more, please!
  Let me stay five minutes more!
Can't I just finish the castle
  I'm building here on the floor?
Can't I just finish the story
  I'm reading here in my book?
Can't I just finish this bead-chain –
  It almost is finished, look!
Can't I just finish this game, please?
  When a game's once begun
It's a pity never to find out
  Whether you've lost or won.
Can't I just stay five minutes?
  Well, can't I stay just four?

Three minutes, then? Two minutes?
Can't I stay one minute more?

Eleanor Farjeon

22nd

Five Brave Firefighters

Five brave firefighters, standing in a row.
"ONE, TWO, THREE, FOUR, FIVE" they go.
  The alarm going BRIIIING!
  They all give a shout,
And jump up on the engine
To put the fire out.

Anon.

23rd

A Millennium Prayer

More people, more computers
More cars, more planes
More war, more pollution
More gadgets, more nuclear, solar and wind power
More selfishness.

No wild animals or trees or birds or insects
No petrol, no oil
No coal, no food
No water.

No hope, no fish
No air, no room
No space, no freedom
No peace, no life
No prayers.

Too little, too much
Too little, too much
Too little, too much
Too little, too much
Lord help us. Amen

Giles Littlewood, age 7

24th

The Coat

I patched my coat with sunlight.
It lasted for a day.
I patched my coat with moonlight,
But the lining came away.
I patched my coat with lightning
And it flew off in a storm

I patched my coat with darkness:
That coat has kept me warm.

Dennis Lee

A Word

A word is dead
When it is said,
Some say.

I say it just
Begins to live
That day.

Emily Dickinson

In the Mirror

In the mirror
On the wall,
There's a face
I always see;
Round and pink,
And rather small,
Looking back again
At me.

It is very
Rude to stare,
But she never
Thinks of that,
For her eyes are
Always there;
What can she be
Looking at?

Elizabeth Fleming

My Old Guitar

I like to play my old guitar,
Strum, strum, strum –
Sometimes with my fingers,
Sometimes with my thumb.

I like to sit around and sing,
And dream that I'm a star.
I like to sit and sing and dream
And play my old guitar.

Wendy Cope

The Tutor

A Tutor who tooted the flute
Tried to teach two young tooters to toot,
    Said the two to the Tutor,
    "Is it harder to toot, or
To tutor two tooters to toot?"

Carolyn Wells

29th

Angelica the Doorkeeper

The falcon soars
The town's gates are even higher

Angelica's their doorkeeper
She's wound the sun around her head
She's tied the moon around her waist

She's hung herself with stars.

Anon.

(Translated from the Serbian by Anne Pennington)

30th

Winter

In the night,
Came a white horse to visit.
His hooves made no sound
As he covered the ground
And snow filled the land with its spirit.

Andrew Fusek Peters

31st

Night Cat

She's there by the fence
but you mustn't call out,
like a scoop of night
or a water shadow
tense for flight
she'll twist and go,
don't open your mouth –
the moon's so close
that the stars blow out –
you turn   she's gone
leaving that patch
where the moon shone

leaving the empty
dress of night
with the stars picked out
and you alone.

Helen Dunmore

February

No Returns

A pinch and a punch
For the first of the month –
And no returns.

A push and a kick
For being too quick –
And no returns.

A boot and a blow
For being so slow –
And no returns.

A slap in the eye
For being so sly –
And no returns.

This knock is the last
Because I am so fast –
And no returns.

Anon.

2nd

Hopping Frog

Hopping frog, hop here and be seen,
 I'll not pelt you with stick or stone:
Your cap is laced and your coat is green;
 Goodbye, we'll let each other alone.

Christina Rossetti

Haiku

A discovery!
On my frog's smooth, green belly
There sits no button.

Yayû

The Hen

In the waiting room of the railway,
Not built for it,
A hen
Walks up and down.
Where, where has the stationmaster gone?
Surely no one
Will harm this hen?
Let us hope not! Then,
Out loud, let us say:
Our sympathy goes out to it
Even here, where it's in the way!

Christian Morgenstern
(Translated from the German by
W. D. Snodgrass and Lore Segal)

The Old Person of Ware

There was an Old Person of Ware,
Who rode on the back of a bear:
When they ask'd, "Does it trot?"
He said, "Certainly not!
He's a Moppsikon Floppsikon bear!"

Edward Lear

A Cheerful Old Bear at the Zoo

A cheerful old bear at the Zoo
Could always find something to do.
When it bored him to go
On a walk to and fro
He reversed it, and walked fro and to.

Lewis Carroll

I'm talking about machines

I'm talking about machines.
New machines
Old machines
Shiny machines
Dull machines.

I'm talking about machines.
Gold machines
Silver machines
Green machines
Red machines.

I'm talking about machines.
Big machines
Small machines
Rigid machines
Flexible machines.

I'm talking about machines.
Blow-up machines
Spiky machines
Thin machines
Fat machines.

Now do you get it?
I'm talking about
MACHINES!!!!!!

Oliver Young, age 8

When You Meet Your Friend

When you meet your friend,
your face brightens—
you have struck gold.

Kassia,
Greece (9th century)

Bobby Shaftoe

Bobby Shaftoe's gone to sea,
Silver buckles at his knee;
He'll come back and marry me,
    Bonny Bobby Shaftoe.

Bobby Shaftoe's bright and fair,
Combing down his yellow hair,
He's my ain for evermair,
    Bonny Bobby Shaftoe.

Bobby Shaftoe's tall and slim,
He's always dressed so neat and trim,
The ladies they all keek at him,
    Bonny Bobby Shaftoe.

February

Bobby Shaftoe's getten a bairn
For to dandle in his arm;
In his arm and on his knee,
    Bobby Shaftoe loves me.

Anon.

10th

Noise

Billy is blowing his trumpet;
Bertie is banging a tin;
Betty is crying for Mummy
And Bob has pricked Ben with a pin.
Baby is crying out loudly;
He's out on the lawn in his pram.
I am the only one silent
And I've eaten all of the jam.

Anon.

Ode to a Sneeze

I sneezed a sneeze into the air,
It fell to earth I know not where,
But hard and froze were the looks of those
In whose vicinity I snooze.

Anon.

The Story of Flying Robert

When the rain comes tumbling down
In the country or the town,
All good little girls and boys
Stay at home and mind their toys.
Robert thought – "No, when it pours,
It is better out of doors."
Rain it did, and in a minute
Bob was in it.

What a wind! Oh! How it whistles
Through the trees and flow'rs and thistles!
It has caught his red umbrella;
It has caught him, silly fellow;
Up he flies
To the skies.
No one heard his screams and cries,
Through the clouds the rude wind bore him,

And his hat flew on before him.
Soon they got to such a height,
They were nearly out of sight!
And the hat went up so high,
That it really touch'd the sky.
No one ever yet could tell
Where they stopp'd, or where they fell:
Only, this one thing is plain,
Bob was never seen again!

Heinrich Hoffman

13th

Chips

Out of the paper bag
Comes the hot breath of the chips
And I shall blow on them
To stop them burning my lips.

Before I leave the counter
The woman shakes
Raindrops of vinegar on them
And salty snowflakes.

Outside the frosty pavements
Are slippery as a slide
But the chips and I
Are warm inside.

Stanley Cook

Porcupine Valentine

Porcupine, oh Porcupine,
Will you be my Valentine?
The touch of your quills sends chills down my spines.
My heart skips a beat whenever we meet.
I love the way you start to rattle
When you stamp your tiny feet.
I adore your sharp claws,
I pine for your spines.
Please be mine,
Porcupine
Valentine.

Jane Clarke

15th

The Rain

Rain on the green grass,
And rain on the tree,
And rain on the house-top.
But not upon me!

Anon.

16th

Grey Goose and Gander

Grey goose and gander,
 Waft your wings together,
And carry the good king's daughter
 Over the one strand river.

Anon.

I Had a Little Horse

I had a little horse,
His name was Dappled Grey.
His head was made of gingerbread,
His tail was made of hay.
He could amble, he could trot,
He could carry the mustard pot,
He could amble, he could trot,
Through the old Town of Windsor.

Anon.

Favouritism

When we caught measles
It wasn't fair –
My brother collected
Twice his share.

He counted my spots:
"One hundred and twenty!"
Which sounded to me
As if I had plenty.

Then I counted his –
And what do you think?
He'd two hundred and thirty-eight,
Small, round and pink!

I felt I'd been cheated
So "Count mine again!"
I told him, and scowled
So he dared not complain.

"One hundred and twenty" –
The same as before . . .
In our house, he's youngest
And he always gets more!

Trevor Harvey

Lemon Sole

I lay and heard voices
spin through the house
and there were five minutes to run
for the snow-slewed school bus.

My mother said they had caught it
as she wiped stars from the window –
the frost mended its web
and she put her snow-cool hand to my forehead.

The baby peeked round her skirts
trying to make me laugh
but I said my head hurt
and shut my eyes on her and coughed.

February

My mother kneeled
until her shape hid the whole world.
she buffed up my pillows as she held me.
"Could you eat a lemon sole?" she asked me.

It was her favourite
she would buy it as a treat for us.
I only liked the sound of it
slim, holy and expensive

but I said "Yes, I will eat it"
and I shut my eyes and sailed out
on the noise of sunlight, white sheets
and lemon sole softly being cut up.

Helen Dunmore

There was a Young Lady of Niger

There was a young lady of Niger,
Who smiled as she rode on a tiger;
They came back from the ride
With the lady inside,
And a smile on the face of the tiger.

Edward Lear

The Mouse

I heard a mouse
Bitterly complaining
In a crack of moonlight
Aslant on the floor.

"Little I ask
And that little is not granted.
There are very few crumbs
In the world any more.

"The bread box is tin
And I cannot get in.

"The jam's in a jar
My teeth cannot mar.

"The cheese sits by itself
On the pantry shelf.

"All night I run
Searching and seeking,
All night I run
About on the floor.

"Moonlight is there
And a bare place for dancing,
But no little feast
Is spread any more."

Elizabeth Coatsworth

The Cat of Cats

I am the cat of cats. I am
    The everlasting cat!
Cunning, and old, and sleek as jam,
    The everlasting cat!
I hunt the vermin in the night –
    The everlasting cat!
For I see best without the light –
    The everlasting cat!

William Brighty Rands

Thoughts for a Cold Day

A little bit of blowing,
  A little bit of snow,
A little bit of growing,
  And crocuses will show;
On every twig that's lonely
  A new green leaf will spring;
On every patient tree-top
  A thrush will stop and sing.

Anon.

Swan, Swan, Swan

Swan, swan, swan:
Stretching your neck to the sky as you sing
White feathers floating on green water
Red feet treading the waves as you swim.

Traditional
(Translated from the Chinese by Xia Lu)

Running

What joy to run
without constraint,
not just to get
to where you ain't.
neither to be fast
nor zappy, but simply 'cos
your legs are happy.

Jez Alborough

26th

My Love For You

I know you little,
I love you lots.
My love for you
Would fill ten pots,
Fifteen buckets,
Sixteen cans,
Three teacups
And four dishpans.

Anon.

27th

Thaw

Over the land freckled with snow half-thawed
The speculating rooks at their nests cawed
And saw from elm tops, delicate as flower of grass,
What we below could not see. Winter pass.

Edward Thomas

Rabbit's Spring

Snow
Goes,

Ice
Thaws,

Warm
Paws!

Brian Patten

Thirty Days Hath September

Thirty days hath September,
April, June and November.
All the rest have thirty-one,
Except February alone,
Which has four and twenty-four
Till leap year gives it one day more.

Anon.

March

1st

Parting of the Seasons

Autumn turns auburn
Summer stays fair
Winter goes grey
And then loses its hair

But Spring's locks and tresses
Are pink, blond and blue,
A full head of colours –
With its roots coming through

Stewart Henderson

The Crocus

The golden Crocus reaches up
To catch a sunbeam in her cup.

Walter Crane

3rd

The Caterpillar

Brown and furry
Caterpillar in a hurry,
Take your walk
To the shady leaf, or stalk,
Or what not,
Which may be the chosen spot.
No toad spy you,
Hovering bird of prey pass by you;
Spin and die,
To live again a butterfly.

Christina Rossetti

A Poem with Knickers in It

It's getting spring.
In Holland Park
Trees brazen it out.

Daffodils in a heap
Around their ankles
Like frilly yellow
    Knickers.

Roger McGough

5th

Hedgehog

A hedgehog is prickly. I held a
Hedgehog yesterday. It felt funny.
    It felt funny inside.
It turned my tummy over.

Emma Gregory, age 5

6th

Shaggy Dogs

Two sheepdogs in a field
Looked up and wondered why
A great big flock of woolly sheep
Was cluttering up the sky.

The sheepdogs growled and leapt,
And climbed the slopes of air,
Yapping, snarling, nipping, snapping,
Scattering sheep everywhere.

And when the sky was clear again
They hurried home together
Back to their field to sunbathe
In the warm blue weather.

Richard Edwards

7th

The Song of the Stars

We are the stars which sing,
We sing with our light;
We are the birds of fire,
We fly over the sky.
Our light is a voice;
We make a road for spirits,
For the spirits to pass over.
Among us are three hunters
Who chase a bear;

There never was a time
When they were not hunting.
We look down on the mountains.
This is the Song of the Stars.

Traditional, Passamaquoddy Tribe

8th

Three Little Owls
Who Sang Hymns

There were three little owls in a wood
Who sang hymns whenever they could;
What the words were about
One could never make out,
But one felt it was doing them good.

Anon.

Stepping Stones

Stepping over stepping stones, one, two, three,
Stepping over stepping stones, come with me.
The river's very fast
And the river's very wide
And we'll step on stepping stones
And reach the other side.

Anon.

Queen, Queen Caroline

Queen, Queen Caroline,
Washed her hair in turpentine,
Turpentine to make it shine,
Queen, Queen Caroline.

Anon.

I Asked the Little Boy who Cannot See

I asked the little boy who cannot see,
"And what is colour like?"
"Why, green," said he,
"Is like the rustle when the wind blows through
The forest; running water, that is blue;
And red is like a trumpet sound; and pink
Is like the smell of roses; and I think
That purple must be like a thunderstorm;
And yellow is like something warm;
And white is a pleasant stillness when you lie
And dream."

Anon.

Dumplins

"Janey, you see nobody pass here?"
  "No me friend."
"Sarah, you see nobody pass here?"
  "No me friend."
"Well, one of me dumplins gone."
  "Don't tell me so!"
"One of me dumplins gone."
"Janey, you see nobody pass here?"
  "No, me friend."
"Sarah, you see nobody pass here?"
  "No, me friend."
"Well, two of me dumplins gone."
  "Don't tell me so!"
"Two of me dumplins gone."

Traditional, Caribbean

I Hope

I hope I will not be a fish when I grow up.
The fishermen might catch me
and turn me into a bag of golden fish fingers
or I might go into the fish-and-chip shop
and be fried and eaten.
I would like to be a teacher instead, when I grow up.

Antonia Goldfinger, age 7

14th

Question

Do you love me
Or do you not?
You told me once
But I forgot.

Anon.

Just Doing

Your legs know how to walk
Your eyes know how to cry
Your mouth knows how to talk
Your heart knows how to fly.

Stephen Bowkett

16th

I Like Silver

I like silver
I like brass
I like looking
In the looking-glass.

I like rubies
I like pearls
I like wearing
My hair in curls.

Anon.

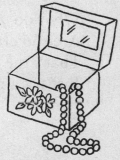

Eat Your Veg

Go on, try the artichoke,
Yes I agree they look
A bit unappetising,
But that TV cook

That you like, gave us the recipe,
And it doesn't taste too bad,
Well how about the peas then?
They're the best *I've* ever had.

What do you mean onions and peppers,
Are too crunchy when you chew?
That's the lamest excuse ever,
Just try a piece . . . won't you?

Those tomatoes are full of vitamins,
Oh yes, you hate the seeds,
Will you taste the aubergine?
Then how about some swedes?

Daddy's done these parsnips specially,
Would you like a wedge?
Oh, come on, don't be difficult,
Mummy, eat your veg.

Valerie Bloom

Mary Had a Little Lamb

Mary had a little lamb,
A lobster, and some prunes,
A glass of milk, a piece of pie,
And then some macaroons.

It made the busy waiters grin
To see her order so,
And when they carried Mary out,
Her face was white as snow.

Anon.

The Prayer of the Ox

Dear God, give me time.
Men are always so driven!
Make them understand that I can never hurry.
Give me time to eat.
Give me time to plod.
Give me time to sleep.
Give me time to think.

Amen

Carmen Bernos de Gasztold

The Secret Song

Who saw the petals
     drop from the rose?
I, said the spider,
But nobody knows.

Who saw the sunset
     flash on a bird?
I, said the fish,
But nobody heard.

Who saw the fog
     come over the sea?
I, said the sea pigeon,
Only me.

Who saw the first
  green light of the sun?
I, said the night owl,
The only one.

Who saw the moss
  creep over the stone?
I, said the grey fox,
All alone.

Margaret Wise Brown

Five Old Fishermen

Five old fishermen
Sitting on a bridge
One caught a tiddler
One caught a fridge.

One caught a tadpole
One caught an eel
And the fifth one caught
A perambulator wheel.

Anon.

Bumpty Dumpty

Bumpty Dumpty sat on a wall,
Bumpty had a Sindy Doll.
    All the King's horses
    And all the King's men
Asked Bumpty to swop it for a Star Wars pen.

John Rice

Grandma's Easter Eggs

"At Eastertime," Gran said to me,
"It was our special thrill
to paint a dozen hard-boiled eggs
and roll them down a hill.
Down the grassy slope we ran
As fast as we could go,
But we never ever caught those eggs
So very long ago," – SIGH –
"so very long ago . . ."

Wes Magee

In Marble Walls as White as Milk

In marble walls as white as milk,
Lined with a skin as soft as silk;
Within a fountain crystal clear,
A golden apple does appear.
No doors there are to this stronghold,
Yet thieves break in and steal the gold.

Anon.

25th

Something About Me

There's something about me
That I'm knowing.
There's something about me
That isn't showing.

I'm growing!

Anon.

Four Ducks on a Pond

Four ducks on a pond,
A grass bank beyond,
A blue sky of Spring,
White clouds on the wing;
What a little thing
To remember for years –
To remember with tears.

William Allingham

The Ptarmigan

The ptarmigan is strange
As strange as he can be;
Never sits on ptelephone poles
Or roosts upon a ptree.
And the way he ptakes pto spelling
Is the strangest thing pto me.

Anon.

The Bestest Bear Song

Oh,
this is the
bear,
the very best
bear,
the best *bestest* best
bear
of all.
It's lost one leg
and it's lost one eye
and it's spotty
and it's grotty
and it's small.
But
this is the
bear,

the very best
    bear,
the best *bestest* best
    bear
    of all.
        Yes, Sir!

Wes Magee

You Don't Frighten Me!

When I get frightened:

I stack,
I pack,
I pile,
I file
All my teddies around my bed

And like soldiers at attention
They offer me a wall of protection.

Then I skip into my bed,
Squeeze deep down into my duvet
And whisper,
"Come on Darkness,
you big, black, bullying,
bubble of trouble,
I'm ready with my teddies
And you don't frighten me!"

Ian Souter

The Farmer and the Queen

"She's coming," the farmer said to the owl.
"Oh, what shall I, what shall I do?
Shall I bow when she comes?
Shall I twiddle my thumbs?"
　　The owl asked, "Who?"

"The Queen, the Queen, the royal Queen –
She'll pass the farm today.
Shall I salute?" he asked the horse.
　　The horse said, "Nay."

"Shall I give her a gift?" he asked the wren.
"A lovely memento for her to keep?
An egg or a peach or an ear of corn?"
　　The wren said, "Cheap."

"But should I curtsy or should I cheer?
Oh, here's her carriage now.
What should I do?" he asked the dog.
    The dog said, "Bow."

And so he did, and so she passed,
Oh, tra lala lala,
"She smiled, she did!" he told the sheep.
    The sheep said, "Bah."

Shel Silverstein

A Race

A Daisy and a Buttercup
  Agreed to have a race,
A Squirrel was to be the judge
  A mile off from the place.

The Squirrel waited patiently
  Until the day was done –
Perhaps he is there waiting still,
  You see – they couldn't run.

Mrs Molesworth (1888)

April

1st

Adam and Eve and Pinch-Me

Adam and Eve and Pinch-me
Went down to the river to bathe.
Adam and Eve were drowned –
Who do you think was saved?

Anon.

Poplars

Seven lovely poplars
Swaying in the breeze.
Seven softly sighing
Tall and slender trees.

Silvered by the moonlight
Pointing to the sky:
Look, like leafy spears, they
Hold the stars on high.

Anon.

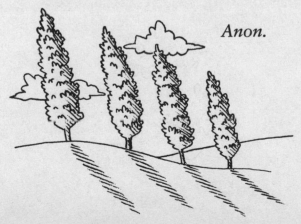

The Cuckoo

If the cuckoo were
Lovely blossoms I would pluck
One sweet note from her!

Traditional,
Japanese (18th century)
(Translated by Kenneth Yasuda)

Nobody Loves Me

Nobody loves me,
Everybody hates me,
I think I'll go and eat worms.

Big fat squishy ones,
Little thin skinny ones,
See how they wriggle and squirm.

Bite their heads off.
"Schlurp!" they're lovely,
Throw their tails away.

Nobody knows
How big I grows
On worms three times a day.

Anon.

5th

Rain Clouds

Along a road
Not built by man
There winds a silent
Caravan
Of camel-clouds
Whose humped grey backs
Are weighted down
With heavy packs
Of long-awaited,
Precious rain

To make the old earth
Young again,
And dress her shabby
Fields and hills
In green grass silk
With wild-flower frills.

Elizabeth-Ellen Long

Watch the Puddles

"Watch the puddles,"
said Mum.
I did,
I watched them all day long.
But the puddles didn't do anything.
Just lay there in the playground.
They didn't sing,
they didn't dance,

they didn't run . . .
they weren't much fun.
Just splashed themselves
all over me,
till I was soaked
from head to toe.
"Now look what you've done,"
said Mum.

Dave Ward

7th

Before the Days of Noah

Before the days of Noah
before he built his ark
seagulls sang like nightingales
and lions sang like larks.
The tortoise had a mighty roar

The cockerel had a moo
kitten always eeyored
and elephants just mewed.
  It was the way the world was
  . . . when owls had a bark
  and dogs did awful crowings
  whilst running round the park.
Horses baaed like baa lambs
ducks could all miaow
and animals had voices
quite different from now!
But, came the day of flooding
and all the world was dark
the animals got weary
of living in the ark –
  So they swapped around their voices
  a trumpet for a mew
a silly sort of pastime
when nothing much to do.
But when the flood had ended
and the world was nice and dry
the creatures had forgotten
how once they hissed or cried.

So they kept their brand-new voices
    forgot the days before
– when lions used to giggle
and gerbils used to roar.

Peter Dixon

The Milk Jug
(The Kitten Speaks)

The Gentle Milk Jug blue and white
I love with all my soul;
She pours herself with all her might
To fill my breakfast bowl.

April

All day she sits upon the shelf,
She does not jump or climb –
She only waits to pour herself
When 'tis my suppertime.

And when the Jug is empty quite,
I shall not mew in vain,
The Friendly Cow all red and white,
Will fill her up again.

Oliver Herford

The Cow

The friendly cow, all red and white,
I love with all my heart:
She gives me cream with all her might,
To eat with apple-tart.

She wanders lowing here and there,
And yet she cannot stray,
All in the pleasant open air,
The pleasant light of day;

And blown by all the winds that pass
And wet with all the showers,
She walks among the meadow grass
And eats the meadow flowers.

Robert Louis Stevenson

Caterpillar

The feet of the
Caterpillar
Do not patter
As he passes
Like the clever
Quick paws
Of the squirrel,
But they ripple,
Stepping one pair
After another
And another,
And they travel
With his whole
Long caravan
Of bristles

Down the brown
Twig, to a
Greener midsummer
Dinner.

Valerie Worth

Prayer of the Butterfly

Lord!
Where was I?
Oh yes! This flower, this sun,
Thank You! Your world is beautiful!
This scent of roses . . .
Where was I?
A drop of dew
Rolls to sparkle in a lily's heart.
I have to go . . .
Where? I do not know!

The wind has painted fancies
On my wings.
Fancies . . .
Where was I?
Oh yes! Lord,
I had something to tell you:

Carmen Bernos de Gasztold

12th

This Tooth

I jiggled it
jaggled it
jerked it.

I pushed
   and pulled
   and poked it.

But –

As soon as I stopped,
And left it alone,
This tooth came out
On its very own!

Lee Bennett Hopkins

A Musical Family

I can play the piano.
I am nearly three.
I can play the long white note
That Mum calls Middle C.

Dad can play the clarinet.
My sister plays the fiddle,
But I'm the one who hits the piano
Slap bang in the middle.

John Mole

I Saw Esau

I saw Esau sawing wood,
And Esau saw I saw him;
Though Esau saw I saw him saw,
Still Esau went on sawing.

Anon.

Egg

I am an egg living in a world where egg beating is allowed, even encouraged, and so I am whipped round and round, until I am dizzy with the pain and longing for those shy days before I came out of my shell.

Coral Rumble

Spring

Waking up from hibernation,
Green shoots sprouting
And flowers blooming
Are not so much a Spring . . .
More a long slow gentle stretch
Reaching towards the sun of Summer.

Paul Cookson

Moonlight, Summer Moonlight

'Tis moonlight, summer moonlight,
All soft and still and fair;
The silent time of midnight
Shines sweetly everywhere,

But most where trees are sending
Their breezy boughs on high,
Or stooping low are lending
A shelter from the sky.

Emily Brontë

18th

The Night Will Never Stay

The night will never stay,
  The night will still go by,
Though with a million stars
  You pin it to the sky,
Though you bind it with the blowing wind
  And buckle it with the moon,
The night will slip away
  Like sorrow or a tune.

Eleanor Farjeon

19th

A Good Night Out
(for the Dog)

There once was a man of Bengal,
Who was asked to a fancy dress ball;
   He murmured, "I'll risk it
   And go as a biscuit" –
But a dog ate him up in the hall.

Anon.

It Wasn't Me

It wasn't me, my cup just fell,
The plate jumped on the floor,
The window cracked all by itself
And then it slammed the door.

I didn't punch, my hand just slipped
And curled into a fist.
He happened to come walking by,
I happened not to miss.

It wasn't me who talked in class,
I didn't steal that pen,
If someone says they saw me cheat
They've got it wrong again.

It wasn't me, it's not my fault!
Why do I get the blame?
The naughty child who does these things
Has pinched my face and name.

Steve Turner

A Saying from Zimbabwe

If you can walk
You can dance
If you can talk
You can sing

Anon.

The Dragon's Lament
(On the Eve of St George's Day)

It isn't much fun to find out you're a dragon,
I wish I'd been born St George.
I would laze about town, drinking wine from a
flagon,
Then look for poor creatures to scourge.

I'd have a head start with my sword and my
armour,
No dragon would *dare* to advance;
And dozens of maidens I'd save before supper,
If only they'd give me the chance.

I'm the last of my kind;
You would think they'd preserve me,
For I'm tired and I'm flameless and old.
I'll just give a few puffs

And then roll over gently
And hope that the blade isn't cold.

St George, he'll be famous –
But what of the dragon?
Who will remember *my* name?
Ah, such is this world –
They must all have their heroes,
And dragons are always "fair game".

Trevor Harvey

Mississippi said to Missouri

Mississippi said to Missouri,
"If I put on my New Jersey
What will Delaware?"
Virginia said, "Alaska."

Anon.

The Lady of Ryde

There was a young lady of Ryde
Who ate a green apple and died;
The apple fermented
Inside the lamented,
And made cider inside her inside.

Anon.

Jerry Hall

Jerry Hall
Is so small,
A rat could eat him
Hat and all.

Anon.

New Shoes

My shoes are new and squeaky shoes,
They're very shiny, creaky shoes,
I wish I had my leaky shoes
That Mother threw away.

I liked my old, brown, leaky shoes
Much better than these creaky shoes,
These shiny, creaky, squeaky shoes
I've got to wear today.

Anon.

The Literary Cat
Dedicated to my Great Aunt Marie

A fire, peace and a book; all a cat wants.
The book's most important.

When humans don't watch and cats are warm,
Spectacles worn,
open slides the bookcase –
secret.
The Marvellous Adventures of Pussykins
is drawn from the shelf.
Happy now,
purring,
our hero puss not stirring,
purr, purr, purr.

Ranjeet Mohan Guptara, age 10

Happy Songs

Piping down the valleys wild,
   Piping songs of pleasant glee,
On a cloud I saw a child,
   And he, laughing, said to me,

"Pipe a song about a lamb,"
   So I piped with merry cheer;
"Piper, pipe that song again,"
   So I piped, he wept to hear.

"Drop thy pipe, thy happy pipe,
   Sing thy songs of happy cheer."
So I sang the same again,
   While he wept with joy to hear.

"Piper, sit thee down and write
  In a book that all may read."
So he vanish'd from my sight;
  And I pluck'd a hollow reed,

And I made a rural pen,
  And I stained the water clear,
And I wrote my happy songs
  Every child may joy to hear.

William Blake

Ladies and Gentlemen

Ladies and gentlemen come to supper –
Hot boiled beans and very good butter.

Anon.

30th

The Peanut Seller

Peanuts!
Two bags for five!
They brush your teeth,
They curl your hair;
They make you feel
Like a millionaire!

Peanuts!
Two bags for five!

New Orleans' Street Cry

May

1st

May Poem

rain falls

the candyfloss tree
rains confetti &
bridesmaids

pink snowdrifts
lie on the path

Gerda Mayer

2nd

Wake, Butterfly

Wake, butterfly –
It's late, we've miles
To go together.

Basho (1644–1694)

Full Moon

She was wearing the coral taffeta trousers
Someone had brought her from Isfahan,
And the little gold coat with pomegranate blossoms,
And the coral-hafted feather fan;
But she ran down a Kentish lane in the moonlight,
And skipped in the pool of the moon as she ran.

She cared not a rap for all the big planets,
For Betelgeuse or Alderbaran,
And all the big planets cared nothing for her,
That small impertinent charlatan,
As she climbed on a Kentish stile in the moonlight,
And laughed at the sky through the sticks of her fan.

Vita Sackville-West

Bee! I'm expecting you!

Bee! I'm expecting you!
Was saying Yesterday
To Somebody you know
That you were due –

The Frogs Got Home last Week –
Are settled, and at work –
Birds, mostly back –
The clover warm and thick –

You'll get my Letter by
The seventeenth; Reply
Or Better, be with me –
Yours, Fly.

Emily Dickinson

Cat March

He's on my bed
again

next to my ear.

He is purring
he is marching –
left foot up
right foot down
left foot down
right foot up.

I ask my mum why he is marching
And
why he is purring . . .
Mum says it's what cats do.
I ask Mum where
he is going.

She says nowhere
but I know where he is going
                    if
        he does not pack it in.

Peter Dixon

Joe Bright

By day, shut in his workshop,
Joe Bright cuts bits of tin,
And smooths them out and flattens them
Until they're paper thin.

At dusk Joe Bright flies skywards
With boxes, bags and jars,
And on the branches of the dark
He hangs a million stars.

Richard Edwards

Dogs

I had a little dog,
   and my dog was very small.
He licked me in the face,
   and he answered to my call.
Of all the treasures that were mine,
   I loved him best of all.

Frances Cornford

Penny Piece

Sun up high,
sky so blue,
went for a walk,
nothing to do.

Branches sighing,
birds a-twitter,
down in the grass
saw something glitter.

Picked it up:
a simple penny,
nothing special,
one of many.

Kept it with me
all the same,
went on careless
till I came

upon a lake
that lay in a trance,
threw my penny,
watched it dance,

spin and flicker
through the air,
down to meet
the water, where

sleeping surface
gasped awake
as that penny
hit the lake,

sending out
circling shiver,
ripples racing,
liquid quiver,

till at last
the glassy pane
slept in silence
once again.

Lake asleep
and penny gone,
made a wish
and then walked on.

Tony Mitton

Pearls

Dad gave me a string of pearls for my birthday.
They aren't real pearls but they look real.
They came nested in deep, deep blue velvet
  In a hinged box with a silvery lid.
His sister had some like them when she was my
  age.
She was thrilled.
He thought I'd really like them.
I said I did.

I love the box.

Jean Little

The Swan

Swan swam over the sea –
Swim, swan, swim;
Swan swam back again,
Well swum, swan.

Anon.

11th

Me
and
Amanda
meander
like
rivers
that
run
to
the
sea.
We
wander
at
random
we're
always
in
tandem:
meandering
Mandy
and
Me.

Me and Amanda

Colin West

The Shepherd

How sweet is the shepherd's sweet lot!
From the morn to the evening he strays;
He shall follow his sheep all the day,
And his tongue shall be filled with praise.

For he hears the lamb's innocent call,
And he hears the ewe's tender reply;
He is watchful while they are in peace,
For they know when their shepherd is nigh.

William Blake

Evening Red and Morning Grey

Evening red and morning grey
Are the signs of a bonny day.
Evening grey and morning red
Bring down rain on the farmer's head.

Anon.

The Fisherman's Wife

When I am alone,
The wind in the pine trees
Is like the shuffling of waves
Upon the wooden sides of a boat.

Amy Lowell

Poem for the Last Day of Football Season

Dreams in tatters
Hopes in rags
Blown away
Like paper bags

Early exits
From each cup
My team down
Your team up

Shadows lengthen
The worst I fear
But I'll be back
Same time next year.

Paul Cookson

Me and the Ball and the Wall

A proper game takes twenty-two
For five-a-side just ten will do
I'd be happy with four, or three
Or even two, a mate and me
But no one's here to play at all
Just me
And the ball
And the wall

Paul Bright

One

Only one of me
And nobody can get a second one
From a photocopy machine.

Nobody has the fingerprints I have.
Nobody can cry my tears, or laugh my laugh
Or have my expectancy when I wait.

But anybody can mimic my dance with my dog.
Anybody can howl how I sing out of tune.
And mirrors can show me multiplied
Many times, say, dressed up in red
Or dressed up in grey.

Nobody can get into my clothes for me
Or feel my fall for me, or do my running.
Nobody hears my music for me, either.
I am just this one.
Nobody else makes the words
I shape with sound, when I talk.

But anybody can act how I stutter in a rage.
Anybody can copy echoes I make.
And mirrors can show me multiplied
Many times, say, dressed up in green
Or dressed up in blue.

James Berry

I'm Nobody

I'm Nobody! Who are you?
Are you – Nobody – too?
Then there's a pair of us! Don't tell!
They'd banish us – you know!
How dreary – to be – Somebody!
How public – like a Frog –
To tell your name – the livelong day –
To an admiring bog!

Emily Dickinson

Gipsy in the Moonlight

Gipsy in the moonlight
Gipsy in the dew
Gipsy never came back
Before the clock struck two.

Walk in gipsy
Walk right in I say
Walk into my parlour
To hear my banjo play.

I love nobody
And nobody loves me
All I want is Mary
To come and dance with me.

Anon.

A Tree Toad Loved a She-toad

A tree toad loved a she-toad
  That lived up in a tree.
She was a three-toed tree toad
  But a two-toed toad was he.
The two-toed toad tried to win
  The she-toad's friendly nod,
For the two-toed toad loved the ground
  On which the three-toed toad trod.
But no matter how the two-toed tree toad tried,
  He could not please her whim.
In her tree-toad bower,
  With her three-toed power
The she-toad vetoed him.

Anon.

A Big Surprise

For my presents, I said I'd like
Computer games,
A mountain bike,
An electric train
Or a model plane
But most of all
I'd like a bike.

I opened my presents
And what did I find there?
A hand knitted hat
And a squeaky bear,
More underpants from my aunts
And socks (grey, one pair).

I said "thank you" nicely,
I tried to smile

But what was I thinking
All the while?
I was thinking
I wanted computer games,
A mountain bike,
An electric train
Or a model plane
But most of all
I'd have liked
A bike.

"There's just one last thing
to unwrap," they said.
"It's a big surprise
we've kept it in the shed.
It's special, it comes with love
From the lot of us . . ."

Now I'm the only kid in school
With my own hippopotamus.

Michaela Morgan

22nd

Baby Talk

The fledglings have a language
That is all their own.
They lisp in broken syllables
In a high, clear tone.
Each bird learns first a single word
Quite long for a beginner,
But says it very plainly,
"Dinner
      Dinner
            Dinner."

Anna Bird Stewart

On a Bad Singer

Swans sing before they die – 'twere no bad thing
Should certain persons die before they sing.

Samuel Taylor Coleridge

Small Things

Dear Father
hear and bless
Thy beasts and singing birds:
And guard with tenderness
small things
that have no words.

Anon.

Short Poem

I am a very tiny verse,
Noticed by no one at all,
My ending is unhappy
Because I am so sma

Andrew Fusek Peters

26ᵗʰ

Teaching Baby Arithmetic

If I give you one kiss, then another one,
That's addition.
Then, if I take some kisses from you,
That's subtraction.
Now, if I give you twice as many kisses,
That's multiplication.

We can't do division because
I'm not sharing you with anyone.

Mike Jubb

27th

I Had a Little Nut Tree

I had a little nut tree,
Nothing would it bear
But a silver nutmeg
And a golden pear;
The King of Spain's daughter
Came to visit me,
And all for the sake of
My little nut tree.
I skipped over water,
I danced over sea,
And all the birds in the air
Couldn't catch me.

Traditional

Wake Up

Wake up

Morning
Has
Galloped
Bareback
All night to
Get here

Zaro Weil

It's Nice . . .

It's nice to be important
But it's more important to be nice.

Anon.

What Do You Suppose?

What do you suppose?
A bee sat on my nose.
Then what do you think?
He gave me a wink
And said, "I beg your pardon,
I thought you were the garden."

Anon.

31st

Big Fat Budgie

I'm a big fat budgie,
   I don't do a lot.
Might park on my perch.
  Might peck in my pot.
      Might peek at my mirror.
  Might ring my bell.
Might peer through the bars of my fat budgie cell.
    Might say "Who's a pretty boy then?"
    Might not.
  I'm a big fat budgie.
    I don't do a lot.

Michaela Morgan

June

1st

If I Were an Apple

If I were an apple
And grew upon a tree,
I think I'd fall down
On a good boy like me.
I wouldn't stay there
Giving nobody joy;
I'd fall down at once
And say, "Eat me, my boy."

Anon.

2nd

An Interesting Fact About One of my Relatives

My

great great great great
great great great great
great great great great
great great great great
great great great great
great great great great
great great great great

grandad is very old.

Ian McMillan

3rd

My Granny's Gairden

I mind my granny's gairden
It was braw
And then she moved,
And noo she lives
In a cooncil flat
And aw she has
Is a windae box.

Caroline Byrne, age 9

4th

When I was Three

When I was three I had a friend
Who asked me why bananas bend,
I told him why, but now I'm four
I'm not so sure . . .

Richard Edwards

5th

Until I Saw the Sea

Until I saw the sea
I did not know
That wind
Could wrinkle water so.

I never knew
That sun
Could splinter a whole sea of blue.

Nor
Did I know before
A sea breathes in and out
Upon a shore.

Lilian Moore

Minnie and Winnie

Minnie and Winnie
 Slept in a shell.
 Sleep, little ladies!
And they slept well.

Pink was the shell within,
 Silver without;
Sounds of the great sea
 Wander'd about

Sleep, little ladies!
 Wake not soon!
 Echo on echo
Dies to the moon.

Two bright stars
Peep'd in the shell.
"What are they dreaming of
  Who can tell?"

Started a green linnet
  Out of the croft;
Wake, little ladies,
  The sun is aloft!

Alfred, Lord Tennyson

7th

The White Seal's Lullaby

Oh! Hush thee, my baby, the night is behind us,
And black are the waters that sparkled so green.
The moon, o'er the combers, looks downward to
   find us
At rest in the hollows that rustle between.

Where billow meets billow, there soft be thy pillow;
Ah, weary wee flipperling, curl at thy ease!
The storm shall not wake thee, nor shark overtake
   thee,
Asleep in the arms of the slow-swinging seas.

Rudyard Kipling

8th

Humming Bird

Humming bird, humming bird, why don't you
    hum?
I do not hum because I am dumb.
Then why are you called humming bird of all
    things?
Because of the noise that I make with my wings.

Odette Thomas

Crescent Moon

The crescent moon
Sails like a small boat,
Sharp at both ends.

As I sit in my small boat
I only see the shining stars
And the dark blue sky.

Traditional, Chinese
(Translated by Xia Lu)

Little Miss Tuckett

Little Miss Tuckett
Sat on a bucket,
Eating some peaches and cream;
There came a grasshopper,
And tried hard to stop her;
But she said, Go away, or I'll scream.

Anon.

The Owl and the Pussy-cat

The Owl and the Pussy-cat went to sea
  In a beautiful pea-green boat,
They took some honey, and plenty of money,
  Wrapped up in a five-pound note.
The Owl looked up to the stars above,
  And sang to a small guitar,
"O lovely Pussy! O Pussy, my love
  What a beautiful Pussy you are,
You are,
You are!
  What a beautiful Pussy you are!"

Pussy said to the Owl, "You elegant fowl!
   How charmingly sweet you sing!
O let us be married! Too long have we tarried:
   But what shall we do for a ring?"
They sailed away, for a year and a day,
   To the land where the Bong-tree grows,
And there in a wood a Piggy-wig stood
   With a ring at the end of his nose,
His nose,
His nose,
   With a ring at the end of his nose.

"Dear Pig, are you willing to sell for one shilling
   Your ring?" Said the Piggy, "I will."
So they took it away, and were married next day
   By the Turkey who lives on the hill.
They dined on mince, and slices of quince,
   Which they ate with a runcible spoon;
And hand in hand, on the edge of the sand,
   They danced by the light of the moon,
The moon,
The moon,
   They danced by the light of the moon.

Edward Lear

The Owl and the Astronaut

The owl and the astronaut
Sailed through space
In their intergalactic ship
They kept hunger at bay
With three pills a day
And drank through a protein drip.
The owl dreamed of mince
And slices of quince
And remarked how life had gone flat;
"It may be all right
To fly faster than light
But I preferred the boat and the cat."

Gareth Owen

Henry and Mary

Henry was a young king,
  Mary was his queen;
He gave her a snowdrop
  On a stalk of green.

Then for all his kindness
  And for all his care
She gave him a new-laid egg
  In the garden there.

"Love, can you sing?"
        "I cannot sing."
"Or tell a tale?"
        "Not one I know."
"Then let us play at queen and king
    As down the garden walks we go."

Robert Graves

There Was a Young Parson Named Perkins

There was a young parson named Perkins
Exceedingly fond of small gherkins
One summer at tea
He ate forty-three,
Which pickled his internal workings.

Anon.

Molly, My Sister, and I Fell Out

Molly, my sister, and I fell out,
And what do you think it was all about?
She loved coffee and I loved tea,
And that was the reason we couldn't agree.

Anon.

My Sister Ate an Orange

My sister ate an orange,
I'm astonished that she did,
She swallowed it completely,
She's a disconcerting kid.

My sister ate an orange,
First she chewed it for awhile,
Then digested it entirely
With a silly sort of smile.

My sister ate an orange,
It's a novel thing to do,
Then she also ate a yellow
And a purple and a blue.

Jack Prelutsky

My Card for Fathers' Day

This is the card that I've made for my dad.
It's sticky with glue . . . but it's not too bad.

I cut out this ship and then stuck it in
And I drew this shark with a great big fin.

Then I've written as neatly as I can
"With love to my dad. He's the world's best man!"

This is the card that I'll give to my dad.
It's sticky with glue . . . but it's not too bad.

Wes Magee

Johnny Come Over the Water

Johnny come over the water
And make the sun shine through.
Johnny come over the water
And paint the sky with blue.

Cover the field and the meadow
With flowers of red and gold,
And cover with leaves the simple trees
That stand so bare and cold.

Johnny come over the water,
Turn the white grass to hay.
It's winter, winter all the year
Since you went away.

Charles Causley

The Shadow Tree

I'd love to sit
   On the highest branch
But it's much too high
   For me;

So I sit on the grass
   Where the shadow falls,
On the top of
   The shadow tree.

Ilo Orleans

Deep in White Blossoms

Deep in white blossoms,
Perky about his prospects,
The summer's first wasp!

Matt Simpson

Where the Bee Sucks

Where the bee sucks, there suck I:
In a cowslip's bell I lie:
There I couch when owls do cry.
On the bat's back I do fly
After summer merrily.
Merrily, merrily shall I live now
Under the blossom that hangs on the bough.

William Shakespeare

Cobbler, Cobbler

Cobbler, cobbler, mend my shoe.
Get it done by half-past two;
Stitch it up and stitch it down,
And then I'll give you half a crown.

Anon.

The Worm

When the earth is turned in spring
The worms are fat as anything.

And birds come flying all around
To eat the worms right off the ground.

They like worms just as much as I
Like bread and milk and apple pie.

And once, when I was very young,
I put a worm right on my tongue.

I didn't like the taste a bit,
And so I didn't swallow it.

But oh, it makes my mother squirm
Because she *thinks* I ate that worm.

Ralph Bergengren

Predictable

When I come out of school today
I know what Mum is going to say:

How was school?
What did you do?
Who did you play with?
What was for lunch?
How did you get that bruise on your knee?
Why is it a secret?
Please tell me.

When I come out of school today
I know what I am going to say:

Can't remember.

Andrea Shavick

Dandelion

I am the seed of the dandelion
My flower is a ball of feathers
When the wind blows gently
I leave the mother I love

I fly and fly
Anywhere can become my home
When I fly
There is my family
There is my home.

David Greygoose
(from the traditional Chinese)

Rosie's Are Red

Rosie's are red, Violet's are blue,
Out on the washing line, open to view!

Matt Simpson

In Beauty May I Walk

In beauty	may I walk
All day long	may I walk
Though the returning seasons	may I walk
Beautifully will I possess again	
Beautifully birds	
Beautifully joyful birds	
On the trail marked with pollen	may I walk
With grasshoppers about my feet	may I walk
With dew about my feet	may I walk
With beauty	may I walk
With beauty before me	may I walk
With beauty behind me	may I walk
With beauty above me	may I walk
With beauty all around me	may I walk
In old age, wandering on a trail of	
beauty, lively,	may I walk

In old age, wandering on a trail of
beauty, living again,   may I walk
It is finished in beauty
It is finished in beauty

Anon.

(Translated from the Navajo by Jerome K. Rothenberg)

This is My Rock

This is my rock,
And here I run
To steal the secret of the sun;
This is my rock,
And here come I
Before the night has swept the sky;

This is my rock,
This is the place
I meet the evening face to face.

David McCord

Fruit Picking

Raspberry, strawberry, gooseberry, plum,
Fruit picking time is really good fun;
Out in the field, in our hats, in the sun,
Raspberry, strawberry, gooseberry, plum.

Gooseberry, strawberry, raspberry, plum,
Carefully picking with finger and thumb;
When the baskets are full our picking is done,
Gooseberry, strawberry, raspberry, plum.

Raspberry, gooseberry, strawberry, plum,
Here is a tune for pickers to hum;
Tap out the beat like the sound of a drum,
Raspberry, gooseberry, strawberry, plum.

Raspberry, strawberry, gooseberry, plum,
Now in our beds when night-time has come
We can think of our wonderful day in the sun,
Raspberry, strawberry, gooseberry, plum.

Jack Ousbey

He Slept Beneath the Moon

He slept beneath the moon
He basked beneath the sun;
He lived a life of going to do
And died with nothing done.

James Albery

July

1st

At the Seaside

When I was down beside the sea
A wooden spade they gave to me
To dig the sandy shore.
My holes were empty like a cup,
In every hole the sea came up
Till it could come no more.

Robert Louis Stevenson

Sea-Weed

Sea-weed sways and sways and swirls
As if swaying were its form of stillness;
And if it flushes against fierce rock
It slips over it as shadows do, without hurting
itself.

D. H. Lawrence

Riddle 7

Light-hearted am I
And sail in the sky
Fancy free
With no strings;
I can fly
Without wings.

What am I?

Barrie Wade

Fireworks

Screeching up high,
Fading away,
All that is left
Is petals in the sky.

Samuel Yardley, age 7

5th

Sounds

Crunching ginger biscuits
is like hearing soldiers tread
marching over gravel
on the inside of your head.

Chewing a marshmallow
is nowhere near as loud.
It's the smaller, sweet equivalent
of swallowing a cloud.

Stewart Henderson

Bug in a Jug

Curious fly,
Vinegar jug,
Slippery edge,
Pickled bug.

Anon.

7th

Every Time I Climb a Tree

Every time I climb a tree
Every time I climb a tree
Every time I climb a tree
I scrape a leg
Or skin a knee
And every time I climb a tree
I find some ants
Or dodge a bee
And get the ants
All over me.

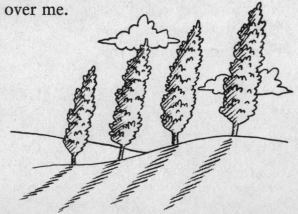

And every time I climb a tree
Where have you been?
They say to me
But don't they know that I am free
Every time I climb a tree?
I like it best
To spot a nest
That has an egg
Or maybe three.

And then I skin
The other leg
But every time I climb a tree
I see a lot of things to see
Swallows rooftops and TV
And all the fields and farms there be
Every time I climb a tree
Though climbing may be good for ants
It isn't awfully good for pants
But still it's pretty good for me
Every time I climb a tree.

David McCord

8th

Pink Azalea

I feel as though
this bush were grown
especially for me.

I feel as though
I almost am
this little flowering tree.

Charlotte Zolotow

9th

Cat Next Door

The cat from next door
Is as quiet as a mouse;
If your front door's ajar,
Then she'll enter your house;
She will creep up the stairs
And she'll search high and low;
When she's seen all she wants,
She'll just turn tail and go.
Unless you're around
You're unlikely to know
That the cat from next door
Who's as quiet as a mouse
Has enjoyed a good sniff
Through the *whole* of your house!

Trevor Harvey

A Three-Legged Friend

They have a three-legged dog
and they call him Clover
and sometimes he falls over
and if he'd had had four legs
maybe they'd have called him
Lucky.

John Hegley

Spider

Spider in the cupboard,
Spin your silver thread,
Spin me out a story
From your tiny head.
Spin me out some kindness,
Cleverness and pluck.
And, also, please,
Along with these,
Spider, spin me luck.

Tony Mitton

12th

If I Had a Donkey

If I had a donkey
That wouldn't go
D'you think I'd wallop him?
No! No! No!
I'd put him in a stable
And keep him nice and warm,
The best little donkey
That ever was born.
Gee up, Neddy,
Gee up, Neddy,
The best little donkey
That ever was born.

Anon.

13th

For Flowers that Bloom About Our Feet

For flowers that bloom about our feet,
Father we thank thee.
For tender grass so fresh, so sweet,
Father we thank thee.
For the song of bird and hum of bee,
For all the things fair we hear or see,
Father in heaven, we thank thee.

Ralph Waldo Emerson

If

If I were oh, so very tall,
I'd walk among the trees
And bend to pick the topmost leaf
As easy as you please.

If I were oh, so very small,
I'd hide myself away,
And creep into a peony cup
To spend the summer's day.

Anon.

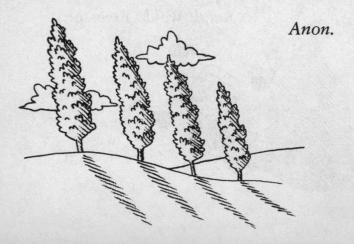

End of Summer Term

Tonight, tonight, the pillow fight,
Tomorrow's the end of school,
Break the dishes, break the chairs,
Trip the teachers on the stairs.

Four more days and we are free
From the school of misery.
No more pencils, no more books,
No more teachers' grumpy looks!

Anon.

16th

For an Autograph Book

Can't think
Brain numb
Inspiration won't come
Can't write
Bad pen
Best wishes – amen.

Anon.

17th

Moving Away

My best friend's leaving school
today,
she's moving somewhere new.
Her house is on the market,
her brother's going too . . .

I saw the lorry loading
her toys
her coat
her hat . . .
her bike
and books
and bedclothes
her hamster and her cat.

She said –
   she'd come and see me,
I said –
   I'd go and see her,
but I don't like these changes
   I liked things as they were.

Peter Dixon

Totteridge Fields

No school tomorrow
So we stayed up later,
Until the sun went down,
Until the familiar field
Grew chill and shadowy.

July

We played at houses quietly;
Loud voices might alert
Parents in both our houses.
The stubbly summer hay
Prickled our bare legs.

Our play was close and secret.
We drank pretend tea
Out of home-made cups
Moulded with squidgy clay
From the forbidden brook.

When they called "Time for bed"
As we knew they would,
We gathered sandals, rug,
Silent, trailed home
Though our adjoining gates

Dreaming about tomorrow.

Anne Harvey

19th

one of the problems of play

every time
before I go out
my mother says
do you have to go
and I say "no" and I go
out but then
I play hard and have to
go and I don't like to
go in when I'm out
so I go out
side when I'm out

Nikki Giovanni

20th

What You Don't Know About Food

Jelly's made from jellyfish.
Spaghetti's really worms.
Ice cream's just some dirty snow
Mixed up with grimy germs.
Bread is made of glue and paste.
So are cakes and pies.
Peanut butter's filled with stuff
Like squashed-up lizard eyes.
And as you eat potato chips,
Remember all the while –
They're slices of the dried-up brain
Of some old crocodile.

Florence Parry Heide

Ice-Cream Man

The ice-cream man coming
Quick, ask ma for ten cents
I going to tell him wait out by the front fence
Quick, go and ask mammy
And make it fast
I ask for money the last time he pass.

Odette Thomas

22nd

On the Beach

They buried their dad
in the golden sands,
buried his legs,
buried his hands,
buried his body
and buried his toes
and left just his face
and a very red nose.

Marian Swinger

The Whale's Hymn

In an ocean before cold dawn broke
Covered by an overcoat
I lay awake in a boat
And heard a whale.

Hearing a song so solemn and so calm
It seemed absurd to feel alarm –
But I had a notion it sang
God's favourite hymn,

And spoke directly to Him.

Brian Patten

Penguins on Ice

Every penguin's mum
can toboggan on her tum.
She can only do that
as she's fluffy and fat:

    It must be nice
    to live on ice.

Every penguin's dad
is happy and glad.
He can slip and slide
and swim and glide:

    It must be nice
    to live on ice.

All penguin chicks
do slippery tricks.
They waddle and fall
but don't mind at all:

It must be nice
to live on ice.

Celia Warren

Crab Dance

Play moonlight
and the red crabs dance
their scuttle-foot dance
on the mud-packed beach

July

Play moonlight
and the red crabs dance
their side-ways dance
to the soft-sea beat

Play moonlight
and the red crabs dance
their bulb-eye dance
their last crab dance.

Grace Nichols

Full Moon

Full moon is the nicest time
For telling 'Nancy story
Except the ones 'bout snake and ghost
Because they are so scary

Hide and seek is nice then too
Because it's light as day
And mamas don't say it's too late
If you go out to play

Odette Thomas

Sunrise

I saw the sun peep over a hill,
He listened very hard until
He heard the cockerel and the lark,
Then he climbed the hill and chased the dark.

Coral Rumble

Under the Greenwood Tree

"Under the greenwood tree,
  Who loves to lie with me,
And turn his merry note
  Unto the sweet bird's throat,
Come hither, come hither, come hither;
      Here shall he see
      No enemy
But winter and rough weather."

William Shakespeare
(Amiens in *As You Like It*)

The Last Steam Train to Margate

Gossssssh
I wissssh
I were
A bussss!
It's muchhhh
Less work
And muchhhh
Less fussss!
I shhhhhould like that
I shhhhhould like that
I shhhhhould like that
I SHHHHHOULD like that!
De-deedle-de
De-deedle-dum

Just look at me
'Cos here I come
Faster and faster
Tickerty-boo, what'll I do
Tearing along, terrible fast
Singing a song, sounding a blast.
WHEE! WHEE! Out of the way!
Goodness me, I can't delay!
You can relax, I have to run.
Follow the tracks into the sun.
Pain in my back, aches in my joints
Tickerty tack, here come the points!
Diddly-dee, diddly-dee
Diddly WIDDLY diddly dee!
Far to go? Not very far.
Little black tunnel (Tickerty – WHAAAAAH!)
Look over there. What can it be?
Lucky old you, clever old me!
Come all this way, never go wrong
Come every day, singing a song
Down to the seaside. Let's have a cheer!
Oh what a train-ride! We're nearly there
We're nearly there, we're nearly there
We're nearly there, we're nearly there

July

So now I'd better slow right down
In half an hour we reach the town
And then you take your buckets and spades
And dig the sands and watch the parades
And swim and paddle and splash in the sea
And eat ice cream and toffee for tea
With ginger beer and orange squash
Hooray we're here, but gosh
I'm tired, oh GOSH I'm tired
Oh GOSSSSH I'M TIRED
OHHHH
GOSSSSSSSSSSSSSSSSSSSH!

Ian Whybrow

30th

His Highness's Dog

I am his Highness's dog at Kew;
Pray, tell me, sir, whose dog are you?

Alexander Pope

Go to Bed Late

Go to bed late,
Stay very small;
Go to bed early,
Grow very tall.

Anon.

August

1ˢᵗ

The Picnic

We brought a rug for sitting on,
Our lunch was in a box.
The sand was warm. We didn't wear
Hats or Shoes or Socks.

Waves came curling up the beach.
We waded. It was fun.
Our sandwiches were different kinds.
I dropped my jelly one.

Dorothy Aldis

My Dad, a String Vest and the Sun

My dad sunbathes in the summer
Sleeping in his stringy vest.
We take it off, play noughts and crosses
In the sunburn on his chest.

Paul Cookson

The Shade-Catchers

I think they were about as high
As haycocks are. They went running by
Catching bits of shade in the sunny street:
"I've got one," cried sister to brother.
    "I've got two." "Now I've got another."
But scudding away on their little bare feet,
They left the shade in the sunny street.

Charlotte Mew

Singing

Little birds sing with their beaks
In the apple trees;
But little crickets in the grass
Are singing with their knees.

Dorothy Aldis

5th

Bilberries

On the hillside
in shaggy coats
hobgoblin fruit
easy for little
hands

Gerda Mayer

Kite

A kite on the ground
is just paper and string
but up in the air
it will dance and sing.
A kite in the air
will dance and will caper
but back on the ground
is just string and paper.

Anon.

Under the Willow

Under the willow
With a leaf stuck in his mouth
The puppy sleeps.

Kobayashi Issa,
Japan (19th century)
(Translated by Lewis Mackenzie)

Catch a Little Rhyme

Once upon a time
I caught a little rhyme

I set it on the floor
but it ran right out the door

I chased it on my bicycle
but it melted to an icicle

I scooped it up in my hat
but it turned into a cat

I caught it by the tail
but it stretched into a whale

I followed it in a boat
but it changed into a goat

When I fed it tin and paper
it became a tall skyscraper

Then it grew into a kite
and flew far out of sight . . .

Eve Merriam

The Frog who Dreamed She was an Opera Singer

There once was a frog
who dreamed she was an opera singer.
She wished so hard she grew a long throat
and a beautiful polkadot green coat

and intense opera singer's eyes.
She even put on a little weight.
but she couldn't grow tall.
She just couldn't grow tall.
She leaped to the Queen Elizabeth Hall,
practising her sonata all the way.
Her voice was promising and lovely.
She couldn't wait to leapfrog on to the stage.
What a presence on the stage!
All the audience in the Queen Elizabeth Hall,
gasped to see one so small sing like that.
Her voice trembled and swelled
and filled with colour.
That frog was a green prima donna.

Jackie Kay

The Joke

The joke you told isn't funny one bit.
It's pointless and dull and wholly lacking in wit.
It's so old and stale, it's beginning to smell!
Besides, it's the one I was going to tell.

Anon.

Triolet

I wish I were a jelly fish
That cannot fall downstairs:
Of all the things I wish to wish
I wish I were a jelly fish
That hasn't any cares,
And doesn't even have to wish
"I wish I were a jelly fish
That cannot fall downstairs."

G. K. Chesterton

Molligan's Rock

Tom, basking on the sunny rock,
   Saw wavering people, very long,
   And heard far-off the wild sea song
And the rock was smooth and the rock was hot.

The goldpenny sun grew huge and fat
   And the salt sea's voice sang round and warm
   A murmurous song of distant storm
But the rock was high and the rock was hot.

All through the afternoon he sat
   And the castles stood till the tide poured through
   And the shimmering light of the long day grew
Round the rock so flat, the rock so hot.

Gerard Benson

Little Donkey Close your Eyes

Little Donkey on the hill
Standing there so very still
Making faces at the skies
Little Donkey close your eyes.

Little Monkey in the tree
Swinging there so merrily
Throwing coconuts at the skies
Little Monkey close your eyes.

Silly Sheep that slowly crop
Night has come and you must stop
Chewing grass beneath the skies
Little Sheep now close your eyes.

August

Little Pig that squeals about
Make no noises with your snout
No more squealing to the skies
Little Pig now close your eyes.

Wild young Birds that sweetly sing
Curve your heads beneath your wing
Dark night covers all the skies
Wild young Birds now close your eyes.

Old black Cat down in the barn
Keeping five small kittens warm
Let the wind blow in the skies
Dear old black Cat close your eyes.

Little Child all tucked in bed
Looking such a sleepy head
Stars are quiet in the skies
Little Child now close your eyes.

Margaret Wise Brown

In the Sun and Shadow

The hands of the sun
are warm on me
when I walk in the open meadow,

But the hands feel cool
when I pass a tree
and walk through the leafy shadow.

Aileen Fisher

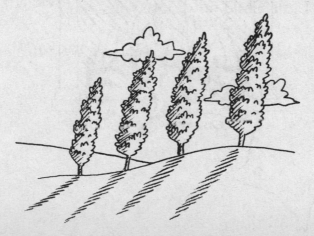

Evensong

Evening comes on, dusk grows cold,
Bunny ears must droop and fold.
Pussy purrs, curls and sighs
Mari darling close your eyes

Traditional, Hungarian

The Mules

In the world of mules
There are no rules.

Ogden Nash

Caribbean Proverbs

A donkey says, this world is not level ground.

A ghost knows who to frighten.

Anon.

from The Mermaid

Who would be
A mermaid fair,
Singing alone,
Combing her hair
Under the sea.
In a golden curl
With a comb of pearl,
On a throne?

I would be a mermaid fair;
I would sing to myself the whole of the day;
With a comb of pearl I would comb my hair;
And still as I comb'd I would sing and say,
"Who is it loves me? Who loves not me?"
I would comb my hair till my ringlets would fall.

Alfred, Lord Tennyson

from The Song of Hiawatha

By the shore of Gitche Gumee,
By the shining Big-Sea-Water,
Stood the wigwam of Nokomis,
Daughter of the Moon, Nokomis.
Dark behind it rose the forest,
Rose the black and gloomy pine-trees,

Rose the firs with cones upon them;
Bright before it beat the water,
Beat the clear and sunny water,
Beat the shining Big-Sea-Water.

Henry Wadsworth Longfellow

20th

Jamaican Summers

Jamaican summers are so hot,
But all over Jamaica
People walk around saying
Dis is cool
Dat is cool
She is cool
Or he's so cool.

August

Jamaican summers are so hot,
Dat all over Jamaica
Parents are always saying
Drink yu coconut water
Drink yu kisko pops
Drink yu mountain water
Yu muss drink a lot.

Jamaican summers are so hot,
Dat all over Jamaica
People chill out in de shade
Sleep under trees
Or travel fe miles
To find cool breeze.

In Jamaica,
Very soon after summer
Comes de winter,
But beware
Let me give yu a warning me friend,
Jamaican winters are so hot.

Benjamin Zephaniah

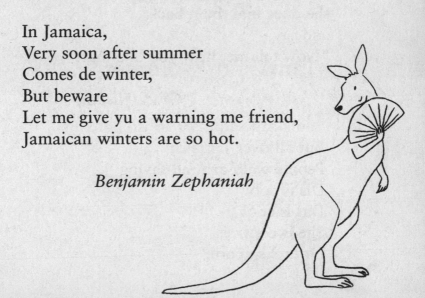

My Cousin Melda

My Cousin Melda
she don't make fun
she ain't afraid of anyone
even mosquitoes
when they bite her
she does bite them back
and say –
"Now tell me, how you like that?"

Grace Nichols

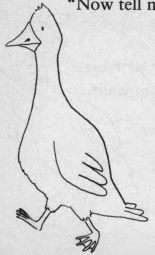

22nd

Shadow Collector

On summer afternoons
    sometimes evenings
I collect shadows . . .
    mainly people
    but sometimes cats and dogs.
I store them away
nice and flat
carefully ironed
between sheets of softest paper,
    free from light
    and prowling shadow thieves.
I collect my shadows from walls and
pavements
    playground spaces
    beaches
    streets
    and gloomy places . . .

Old folk shadows
young and poor
teachers' shadows
(classroom floors).
But one is special
It's big.
It's tall.

And I found it on a palace wall.

Peter Dixon

My Mother Said

My mother said that I never should
Play with the gypsies in the wood;
If I did, she would say,
Naughty girl to disobey.

Anon.

Jessel's Song

I like mas*
I like playing
with my class
jumping up and down
the street
look I feeling so sweet

I like mas
I like the steel
and the brass
jumping up and down
look I feeling so sweet

*mas = carnival

And if you see me
how I looking sharp
with meh costume
up to mark
playing mas in the city
oh how happy I will be

I like mas
I like playing
with my class
jumping up and down
the street

look I feeling so sweet.

Eintou Pearl Springer

25th

Batman's Exercise Video

Pull on the tights
Yeah, pull on the tights
Pull up the trunks
Yeah, pull up the trunks

I said twirl the cape
       twirl the cape
       twirl the cape
       twirl the cape

Pull on the boots
Yeah, pull on the boots
Snap on the mask
Yeah, snap on the mask

I said twirl the cape
    twirl the cape
    twirl the cape
    twirl the cape

Repeat until opponents are fully dazzled . . .

Ian McMillan

Lucky Lion!

It sleeps by day!
How blessed it is,
Lion.

Anon.

Being Trees

"Why not play at being trees?" asks
Mum, "Great fun." So we try and try,
pushing branches sky-high, Jack and I.

He's an English oak, I'm a conker tree:
sparrows and starlings perch whilst
squirrels search in either Jack or me.

Roots spread-out, dig deep,
deep down, "Remember," Mum
says, "trees seldom make a sound."

Swaying, slowly swaying,
Whispering, in a summer breeze . . .

Five-minutes'-worth of calm and peace.

"I'm sure that you're both growing leaves!"
Mum really likes us being trees.

Mike Johnson

28th

Hiding

Behind this tree
You can't see me,
I've made myself thin
So I can fit in.

I'm as still as a photograph,
As quiet as a blink,
I won't sniff or laugh
Just quietly think.

Behind this tree
You can't see me,
I've made myself thin
So I can fit in.

Coral Rumble

I'm Just Going Out for a Moment

I'm just going out for a moment.
Why?
To make a cup of tea.
Why?
Because I'm thirsty.
Why?
Because it's hot.
Why?

Because the sun's shining.
Why?
Because it's summer.
Why?
Because that's when it is.
Why?
Why don't you stop saying why?
Why?
Tea-time why.
High-time-you-stopped-saying-why-time.
What?

Michael Rosen

Banyan Tree

Moonshine tonight, come mek we dance and
   sing,
Moonshine tonight, come mek we dance and sing,
Me deh rock so, yu deh rock so, under banyan
   tree,
Me deh rock so, yu deh rock so, under banyan
   tree.

Ladies mek curtsy, an gentlemen mek bow,
Ladies mek curtsy, an gentlemen mek bow,
Me deh rock so, yu deh rock so, under banyan
   tree,
Me deh rock so, yu deh rock so, under banyan
   tree.
Den we join hans an dance around an roun,
Den we join hans an dance around an roun,

Me deh rock so, yu deh rock so, under banyan
   tree,
Me deh rock so, yu deh rock so, under banyan
   tree.

Traditional, Jamaican

31ˢᵗ

The Stork

I lift my leg, I stretch my leg,
I plant it firm and light.
I lift again, and stretch again
My pace exactly right.
With care I go, so grand and slow,

I move just like a stork;
My eye is bright, my head upright,
And pride is in my walk.

Anon.

September

1st

First Fox

A big fox stands in the spring grass,
Glossy in the sun, chestnut bright,
Plumb centre of the open meadow, a leaf
From a picturebook.

Forepaws delicately nervous,
Thick brush on the grass
He rakes the air for the scent
Of the train rushing by.

My first fox,
Wiped from my eye,
In a moment of train-time.

Pamela Gillilan

Rhyme for Children

I am the seed that slept last night;
This morning I have grown upright.

Within my dream there was a king.
Now he is gone in the wide morning.

September

He had a queen, also a throne.
Waking, I find myself alone.

If I could have that dream again
The seed should grow into a queen

And she should find at her right hand
A king to rule her heart and land:

And I would be the spring which burst
Beside their love and quenched their thirst.

Elizabeth Jennings

3rd

Be Like the Bird

Be like the bird, who
Resting in his flight
On a twig too slight
Feels it bend beneath him,
Yet sings
Knowing he has wings.

Victor Hugo

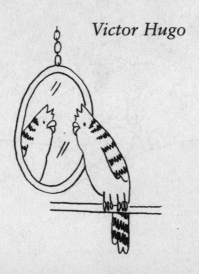

The Swallow

Fly away, fly away, over the sea,
Sun-loving swallow, for summer is done.
Come again, come again, come back to me,
Bringing the summer and bringing the sun.

Christina Rossetti

Round and Round

Rosie paints some dark green hills
Under a sky-blue sky,
Rosie paints a red-faced sun,
Some white doves flying high,
Rosie paints a man of straw
Beside the yellow wheat,
Rosie paints some coal-black crows
That pick around his feet,
Rosie paints a big, grey cloud,
The cloud begins to rain,
The rain makes all her colours run,
Rosie starts again . . .

Richard Edwards

6th

Weather

Dot a dot dot dot a dot dot
Spotting the windowpane.
Spack a spack speck flick a flack fleck
Freckling the windowpane.

A spatter a scatter a wet cat a clatter
A splatter a rumble outside.
Umbrella umbrella umbrella umbrella
Bumbershoot barrel of rain.

Slosh a galosh slosh a galosh
Slither and slather a glide
A puddle a jump a puddle a jump
A puddle a pump aluddle a dump a
Puddmuddle jump in and slide!

Eve Merriam

New Shoes

New shoes new shoes
Red and pink and blue shoes
Tell me what you would choose
If you could buy some.

Buckle shoes bow shoes
Pretty pomty toe shoes
Strappy cappy low shoes
If you could try some.

Bright shoes white shoes
Dandy dance by night shoes
Perhaps a little tight shoes
Like some? So would I.

Flat shoes fat shoes
Stump along like that shoes
Wipe them on the mat shoes –
What's the sort they'll buy.

Anon.

Emma and Rebecca

Emma and Rebecca sit behind us,
And oh, the fuss,
"That's my pen." "Oh no it's mine."
"Shut up Emma." "Shut up yourself."
"What's your phone number?" "What's yours"?

291

"Ain't gonna tell yah."
"Won't tell you mine, then."
"Fine."
"OK, let's work now."
"OK."
And I say, "Shut up you pair," and they say
"Don't tell me, tell her!"

Kelly Bambrick, age 10

Because of Number One

I'll tell you something funny –
The strangest thing under the sun.
There's never an end to numbers,
Because of Number One.

You think you're clever when you count to twenty –
But then there's twenty-one.
So on you go, and thirty comes –
And then comes thirty-one!

You reach a hundred! Then you think
That all your counting's done.
But no! A little voice inside
Says, "Now a hundred-and-one!"

You reach a thousand! Number One
Insists on going on.
You're all worn out. A million comes:
But there's still "A million-and-one".

The person who caused all this trouble
(when I could be out having fun)
Is the man who lived in the dim distant past
And invented Number One!

Pam Gidney

The Surprising Number 37

The number 37 has a special magic to it.
If you multiply 37 x 3, you get   111
If you multiply 37 x 6, you get   222
If you multiply 37 x 9, you get   333
If you multiply 37 x 12, you get   444
If you multiply 37 x 15, you get   555
If you multiply 37 x 18, you get   666
If you multiply 37 x 21, you get   777
If you multiply 37 x 24, you get   888
If you multiply 37 x 27, you get   999

Anon.

Dick's Dog

Dick had a dog
The dog dug
The dog dug deep
How deep did Dick's dog dig?

Dick had a duck
The duck dived
The duck dived deep
How deep did Dick's duck dive?

Dick's duck dived as deep as Dick's dog dug.

Trevor Millum

12th

Animal Rights

Our cat
Won't use the cat-flap
Any more.
He's started to fight
For his Animal Rights
And insists
That he uses the door.

Lindsay MacRae

The Woodchuck

If a woodchuck could chuck
All the wood
That a woodchuck would
How much wood
Could a woodchuck chuck
If a woodchuck would chuck wood?

Anon.

What are Little Boys Made of?

What are little boys made of, made of?
What are little boys made of?
     Frogs and snails
     And puppy-dogs' tails,
That's what little boys are made of.

What are little girls made of, made of?
What are little girls made of?
     Sugar and spice
     And all things nice,
That's what little girls are made of.

Anon.

Whole Duty of Children

A child should always say what's true,
And speak when he is spoken to,
And behave mannerly at table:
At least as far as he is able.

Robert Louis Stevenson

Good and Clever

If all the good people were clever,
　And all clever people were good,
The world would be nicer than ever
　We thought that it possibly could.

But somehow 'tis seldom or never
　The two hit it off as they should,
The good are so harsh to the clever,
　The clever, so rude to the good!

So friends, let it be our endeavour
　To make each by each understood;
For few can be good, like the clever,
　Or clever, so well as the good.

Elizabeth Wordsworth

Big and Little

Big boys do,
Little boys don't.

Big boys will
Little boys won't.

Big boys can,
Little boys can't.

Big boys shall,
Little boys shan't.

Anon.

Prayer

"Lord! Let me catch a fish
So large that even I,
In telling of it afterwards,
Shall have no need to lie."

Anon.

Saturday Night Blues

What do I care for the telly?
Why should I want to play?
What do I care for a story at bedtime
When my team lost today?

Fred Sedgwick

20th

Fishing

There is a fine
Line
Between fishing
And standing
On the bank
Like an idiot.

Gerard Benson

21st

End of a Girl's First Tooth

Once she'd a tooth that wiggled;
Now she's a gap that lisps.
For days she could only suck lollies;
Now she champs peanuts and crithsps.

Roy Fuller

Only one pair of hands

"I wish I was an octopus,"
my teacher said to me.
I didn't understand at first,
but now I think I see.

I only wanted her to read
the story that I wrote,
to sharpen all my pencils,
to button up my coat,
to fix my broken shoelace,
to find my missing shoe,
and one or two more other things
I wanted her to do.

"I wish I was an octopus,"
my teacher said to me.
I didn't understand at first,
but now I think I see.

I told my daddy what she said,
and Daddy understands.
It means that she would like to have a few more
pairs of hands.
But, I don't want an octopus
teaching me instead.
It's bad enough having a teacher
with eyes in the back of her head.

Mike Jubb

I See a Seagull

I see a seagull in the playground.
I see a crisp-bag and a glove;
Grey slides on the grey ice
And a grey sky above.

I see a white bird in the playground
And a pale face in the glass:
A room reflected behind me,
And the rest of the class.

I see a seagull in the playground.
I see it fly away.
A white bird in the grey sky:
The lesson for today.

Allan Ahlberg

Summer is Gone

I have but one story –
The stags are moaning,
The sky is snowing,
Summer is gone.

Quickly the low sun
Goes drifting down
Behind the rollers,
Lifting and long.

The wild geese cry
Down the storm;
The ferns have fallen,
Russet and torn.

The wings of the birds
Are clotted with ice.
I have but one story
Summer is gone.

Anon.

If I were a Queen

If I were a Queen,
   What would I do?
I'd make you King,
   And I'd wait on you.

If I were a King,
   What would I do?
I'd make you Queen,
   For I'd marry you.

Christina Rossetti

26th

Lion King

Topaz stare,
Deep as the stone on
Grandad's watch chain.

Bronze coat,
Dark as heather honey from
A newly opened pot.

Golden mane,
Bright as a king's crown in
The hot yellow sun.

Moira Andrew

Aching Bones

There's nothing badder
  than an adder
      with aching bones.
  He moans and groans,
    and hisses and bites
and gets into fights,
    over nothing.
    So something
        has to be done for the adder
        or he becomes badder and madder.
    But teach him some yoga,
  he'll sway like a cobra:
    tying himself in knots,
        he'll think sweet thoughts.

There's nothing gladder
than an adder
who owns
flexible bones.

Debjani Chatterjee

Our Night Visitor

A bunny came to call last night.
I did not see him – that is right.
But he was there; here's how I know –
He nibbled at my carrot row.

Christina T. Owen

29th

There was an Old Woman Tossed Up in a Basket

There was an old woman tossed up in a basket,
  Seventeen times as high as the moon;
And where she was going, I couldn't but ask it,
  For in her hand she carried a broom.
Old woman, old woman, old woman, quoth I,
  O whither, O whither, O whither so high?
To sweep the cobwebs off the sky!
  Shall I go with you? Aye, by-and-by.

Anon.

The Day that Summer Died

From all around the mourners came
The day that Summer died,
From hill and valley, field and wood
And lane and mountainside.

They did not come in funeral black
But every mourner chose
Gorgeous colours or soft shades
Of russet, yellow, rose.

Horse chestnut, oak and sycamore
Wore robes of gold and red;
The rowan sported scarlet beads;
No bitter tears were shed.

September

Although at dusk the mourners heard,
　　As a small wind softly sighed,
A touch of sadness in the air
　　The day that Summer died.

Vernon Scannell

October

1st

October Boy

If you can catch a leaf, so they say
   As it falls from the tree,
     Glad will you be,
   For a year and a day.

But I say let the leaves lie on the ground.
   I will find my delight
     Galloping right
   Into this rustling mound.

Let others snatch happiness from the trees
   I will jump in this deep
     Mouldering heap
   Up to my knobbly knees.

Virginia Graham

Down by the Station

Down by the station
Early in the morning,
See the little puffer trains
All in a row.
    See the engine driver
    Turn the little handle.

Chug-chug,
      Toot-toot,
Off we go.

Anon.

Mrs Magee

Mrs Magee
Climbed into a tree,
And she only came down to go shopping.
A branch was her bed,
With a leaf on her head –
And whenever it rained, she got sopping.

Dennis Lee

The Tree and the Pool

"I don't want my leaves to drop," said the tree.
"I don't want to freeze," said the pool.
"I don't want to smile," said the sombre man,
"Or ever to cry," said the Fool.

"I don't want to open," said the bud,
"I don't want to end," said the night.
"I don't want to rise," said the neap-tide,
"Or ever to fall," said the kite.

They wished and they murmured and whispered,
They said that to change was a crime,
Then a voice from nowhere answered,
"You must do what I say," said Time.

Brian Patten

Dad and Me

Up in his wardrobe, my dad has a very old base-
   ball glove
That was his when he was a kid.
In my wardrobe, I have an old blanket called Softie
That was mine when I was very little.
Dad never uses his glove anymore
And I don't use Softie.
But Dad doesn't want to throw his glove away
And I don't want to throw away my blanket either.
We just want to keep them.
If you ask us why,
We say we don't know why, we just do.

Jeff Moss

Waiting Both

A star looks down at me,
And says: "Here I and you
Stand, each in our degree:
What do you mean to do, –
    Mean to do?"

I say: "For all I know,
Wait, and let Time go by,
Till my change come," – "Just so."
The star says: "So mean I: –
    So mean I."

Thomas Hardy

7th

from Dream-Pedlary

If there were dreams to sell,
  What would you buy?
Some cost a passing bell;
  Some a light sigh,
That shakes from Life's fresh crown
Only a roseleaf down.
If there were dreams to sell,
Merry and sad to tell,
And the crier rung the bell,
  What would you buy?

Thomas Lovell Beddoes

A Cat called Slumber

In the middle of the night appears
My day-shy tabby with collapsible ears
And I stroke her head so those ears collapse
And she purrs to say that she loves me, perhaps.

Adrian Mitchell

Samantha is Sobbing

Samantha is sobbing
By the playground wall
But why she should be sobbing
No one knows at all.

The sun shines brightly
The sky is blue
But Samantha is sobbing
Oh what shall we do?

Take her to Granny
Who lives down Comfort Lane
Once she gets to Granny's house
She'll never sob again.

She'll kiss her on the top knot
And treat her like a queen
Feed her new potatoes
Beans and margarine.

Gareth Owen

The Older the Violin the Sweeter the Tune

Me granny old
Me granny wise
stories shine like a moon
from inside she eyes.

Me granny can dance
Me granny can sing
But she can't play violin.

Yet she always saying,
"Dih older dih violin
de sweeter de tune."

Me granny must be wiser
than the man in the moon.

John Agard

Under the Woodland Autumn Leaves

Kick up the leaves
What do you see?
Creepy crawlies under the tree,
Busying about where nobody goes
Wriggling about under your toes.
Squirming up, tunnelling down
Active insects building their town.

Margaret Blount

A Fishy Thought

A kipper
With a zipper
Would be neater
For the eater . . .

Vivian French

Jamaican Clap Rhyme

Where your mama gone?
She gone down town.

She take any money?
She take ten pound.

When your mamma come back,
what she gonna bring back?

Hats and frocks and
shoes and socks.

Anon.

Spider

Spider, spider
You and your wife
Me and my wife
Our hands you pinch, pinch
Our hands you bite, bite.

Traditional, New Guinean

Jack in the Sky

Jack popped his head through a door in the sky
Hopped down Memory Street
Raised his hat to the smiling sun
And the friends he chanced to meet.

He danced in the eye of the afternoon
Smiled at all he saw
While the cat on the sun-warmed doorstep purred
And licked her folded paw.

Jane on a swing in the garden green
Her yellow hair flowed free
Smiled at the ghost of brother Jack
That only she could see.

Gareth Owen

Maggie

There was a small maiden named Maggie,
Whose dog was enormous and shaggy;
    The front end of him
    Looked vicious and grim –
But the tail end was friendly and waggy.

Anon.

Old Noah's Ark

Old Noah once he built an ark,
And patched it up with hickory bark.
He anchored it to a great big rock,
And then he began to load his stock.
The animals went in one by one,
The elephant chewing a caraway bun.
The animals went in two by two,
The crocodile and the kangaroo.
The animals went in three by three,
The tall giraffe and the tiny flea,
The animals went in four by four,
The hippopotamus stuck in the door.
The animals went in five by five,
The bees mistook the bear for a hive.
The animals went in six by six,
The monkey was up to his usual tricks.
The animals went in seven by seven,

Said the ant to the elephant, "Who're ye shov'n?"
The animals went in eight by eight,
Some were early and some were late.
The animals went in nine by nine,
They all formed fours and marched in a line.
The animals went in ten by ten,
If you want any more, you can read it again.

Anon.

18th

Words I Like

Billowing, seaboard, ocean, pearl,
Estuary, shale, maroon;
Harlequin, runnel, ripple, swirl,
Labyrinth, lash, lagoon.

Razorbill, cygnet, songbird, kite,
Cormorant, crag, ravine;
Flickering, sun-burst, dappled, flight,
Fiery, dew, serene.

Asteroid, nova, star-dust, moon,
Galaxy, zone, eclipse;
Dynamo, pulsar, planet, rune,
Satellite, spangle, lips.

Boulevard, freeway, turnpike, cruise,
Chevrolet, fin, pavane;
Tomahawk, firecrest, fantail, fuse,
Saskatchewan, Sioux, Cheyenne.

Tenderness, sweetheart, cherish, miss,
Paramour, fond, befriend;
Affection, cosy, cuddle, kiss,
Family, love, the end.

Steve Turner

Mary Had a Crocodile

Mary had a crocodile
That ate a child each day;
But intefering people came
And took her pet away.

Anon.

20th

As to the Restless Brook

Do you suppose the babbling brook
    Would stop and rest its head
If someone got a scoop and took
    The pebbles from its bed?

John Kendrick Bangs

Season Song

Here's a song –
Stags give tongue
Winter snows
Summer goes.

High cold blow
Sun is low
Brief his day
Seas give spray.

Fern clumps redden
Shapes are hidden
Wildgeese raise
Wonted cries.

Cold now girds
Wings of birds
Icy time –
That's my rime.

Anon.
(This version by Flann O'Brien
from the Irish)

22nd

The Night was Growing Old

The night was growing old
  As she trudged through snow and sleet;
And her nose was long and cold,
  And her shoes were full of feet.

Anon.

23rd

Old Meg

Old Meg was a gypsy
She lived on the moors
Her bed was the heather
Her home out of doors.

No breakfast at morn
No dinner at noon
And for her supper
She stared at the moon.

Anon.

There once Was a Plesiosaurus

There once was a plesiosaurus,
Who lived when the world was all porous;
    But it fainted with shame,
When it first heard its name,
And departed long ages before us.

Anon.

Tumbling

In jumping and tumbling
   We spend the whole day,
Till night by arriving
   Has finished our play.

What then? One and all,
   There's no more to be said,
As we tumbled all day,
   So we tumble to bed.

Anon.

O Moon!

O Moon! when I look on your beautiful face,
Careering along through the darkness of space,
The thought has frequently come to my mind,
If ever I'll gaze on your lovely behind.

Anon.

Burying Moses

Moses was very old,
Ninety-eight, my grandpa said,
So we shouldn't cry too much
Now poor old Moses was dead.

Moses used to be black
But he slowly turned grey as a fog
And snuffled and wheezed and snored.
Moses was our old dog.

Each year that people live
Counts for a dog as seven.
"He was a good old boy," said Grandpa,
"He's sure to go to heaven.

"But first we must go and bury him
At the back of the garden shed,
So come and give me a hand;
We'll make him a deep warm bed."

And so we lowered old Moses
Down in the hole Grandpa dug,
And he huddled there in a bundle
Like a dusty old fireside rug.

Then we filled in the hole and patted
The soil down smooth and flat.
"I'll make him a cross," said Grandpa.
"The least we can do is that.

"He'll be wagging his tail in heaven,
So you mustn't be upset . . ."
But grandpa's voice sounded croaky,
And I could see his old cheeks were wet.

Vernon Scannell

Red Boots On

Way down Geneva,
All along Vine,
Deeper than the snow drift
Love's eyes shine:

Mary Lou's walking
In the winter time.

She's got

Red boots on, she's got
Red boots on,
Kicking up the winter
Till the winter's gone.

So

Go by Ontario,
Look down Main,
If you can't find Mary Lou,
Come back again:

Sweet light burning
In winter's flame.

She's got

Snow in her eyes, got
A tingle in her toes
And new red boots on
Wherever she goes

So

All around Lake Street,
Up by St Paul,
Quicker than the white wind
Love takes all:

Mary Lou's walking
In the big snow fall.

October

She's got

Red boots on, she's got
Red boots on,
Kicking up the winter
Till the winter's gone.

        Kit Wright

To a Schoolboy

Ploughman ploughing a level field
His plough a magic tree
An oleaster tree

Ploughing a level field
His ploughshare a grey dove
His goad a sprig of basil
His oxen two stags

Instead of wheat
He's sowing small pearls
Ploughing with a magic feather
A peacock feather.

Anon.

Peter, Peter, Pumpkin Eater

Peter, Peter, pumpkin eater,
Had a wife and couldn't keep her;
He put her in a pumpkin shell,
And there he kept her very well.

Anon.

Three Little Ghostesses

Three little ghostesses,
Sitting on postesses,
Eating buttered toastesses,
Greasing their fistesses,
Up to their wristesses,
Oh, what beastesses
To make such feastesses!

Anon.

November

November

November is a spinner
  Spinning in the mist,
Weaving such a lovely web
  Of gold and amethyst.
In among the shadows
  She spins till close of day,
Then quietly she folds her hands
  And puts her work away.

Margaret Rose

Who's there?

Knock, knock!
Who's there?
cried the spider.
Stand and wait!
But she knew by the
gentle tweak of the web
it was her mate.

Knock, knock!
Who's there?
cried the spider.
Call your name!
But she knew by the
soft tap-tap on the silk
her spiderlings came.

Knock, knock!
Who's there?
cried the spider.
Who goes by?
But she knew by the
shaking of her net
it was the fly.

Judith Nicholls

3rd

Sweet Song for Katie

The white doves are cooing,
Oh! Katie my dear,
In the sun in the morning,
In the spring of the year.
The peace doves are cooing,
Oh! Kate can you hear?

And when you are grown
And summer is high,
Will you listen my darling
To the birds in the sky,
And spread out your wild arms
As if you could fly?

Oh! I ask nothing better
For Katie and me
That we're brave as the new wind
That springs from the sea,
And we sing like the peace doves
In the green mango tree.

For we'll build a new world,
When the cane grass is high,
And peace will drop softly
Like wings from the sky,
And the children will run,
And the wild birds will fly.

And all that I ask now
For Katie and me,
Is a faith that is strong
As the wind off the sea,
Blowing so loud
In the green mango tree,
With a song that is ceaseless
As a dove in a tree.

Dorothy Hewett

Sneezes

When I
sneeze

I don't go
"Achoo!"

Or
"Atishoo!"

I go
"Yar . . . yar . . . yar . . . shar . . . shar . . . sh-sh-sh-ashkeroo!"

I don't think
my sneezes

Ever learned
to spell.

Roger McGough

Fireworks

They rise like sudden fiery flowers
   That burst upon the night,
Then fall to earth in burning showers
   Of crimson, blue and white.

Like buds too wonderful to name,
   Each miracle unfolds,
And catherine-wheels begin to flame
   Like whirling marigolds.

Rockets and Roman candles make
    An orchard of the sky,
Whence magic trees their petals shake
    Upon each gazing eye.

James Reeves

6th

Friendship Poem

Two boys by firelight
One black face the other white,
Friends in the cold night.

James Stevens, age 11

7th

Leaf Lines

As I look at
this Autumn leaf,
fallen from its tree,
I see how it has
ribs and flesh
like you and me.

Tony Mitton

8th

Fog

The fog comes
on little cat feet.
It sits looking
over harbour and city
on silent haunches
and then moves on.

Carl Sandburg

9th

No Shop Does the Bird Use

No shop does the bird use,
no counter nor baker,
but the bush is his orchard,
the grass is his acre,
the ant is his quarry,
the seed is his bread,
and a star is his candle
to light him to bed.

Elizabeth Coatsworth

10th

If You Have Plenty

If you have plenty, be not greedy,
But share it with the poor and needy:
If you have a little, take good care
To give the little birds a share.

Anon.

11th

A Poem About a Wolf Maybe Two Wolves

y
    o
       w
           e
              e
                  e
                    e
he comes running   e
across the field where
he comes running   e
                  e
                e
            e
        e
    e

y   he comes running
  o   across the field where
    w   he comes running
      e
        e
          e
            e
              e
                e

Traditional,
North American Indian

12th

There are Pictures

There are pictures in poems
and poems in pictures

Chinese Proverb

Granny

Through every nook and every cranny
The wind blew in on poor old Granny;
Around her knees, into each ear
(And up her nose as well I fear).

All through the night the wind grew worse,
It nearly made the vicar curse.
The top had fallen off the steeple
Just missing him (and other people).

It blew on him; it blew on beast.
It blew on nun; it blew on priest.
It blew the wig off Auntie Fanny –
But most of all, it blew on Granny.

Spike Milligan

Dreaming the Unicorn

I dreamed I saw the Unicorn
Last night.
It rippled through the forest,
Pearly white,
Breathing a moonlit silence.

Its single horn
Stood shining like a lance.
I saw it toss its head
And snort and prance
And paw the midnight air.
Its mane was like a mass
Of silver hair.

My mind was wild, unclear.
I could not think or speak.
Above my head, I heard the branches creak
And then, from where I stood,
I watched it flicker off into the wood,
Into the velvet space between the trees.

A sudden rush of rapid midnight breeze,
that felt both chill and deep,
awoke me from my sleep,
and there upon the pillow by my head
I found a strand of silver shining thread.

I kept that strand of mane,
I keep it, still,
inside a box upon my window sill.
And when the world hangs heavy
on my brain,
it helps me dream the Unicorn again.

Tony Mitton

15th

New Sounds

New sounds to
walk on
today –

dry
leaves,
talking
in hoarse
whispers,
under bare trees.

Lilian Moore

16th

Song

Don't you ever
you up in the sky
don't you ever get tired
of having the clouds
between you and us?

Traditional, Nootka Indian
(Translated by John Bierhorst)

17th

Getting Back Home

Hang your hat on the peg
Rest up, rest up
Fling your coat on the bed
For you have travelled many miles to see me.

Put your feet on the bench
Rest up, rest up
Heave off your heavy boots
For you have come through winter days to see me.

Settle down by the fire
Rest up, rest up
Lean back and smile at me
For after all this time and travelling
Oh traveller, I'm glad to see you.

Jenny Joseph

Quadrupedremian Song

He dreamt that he saw the Buffalant,
  And the spottified Dromedaraffe,
The blue Camelotamus, lean and gaunt,
  And the wild Tigeroceros calf.

The maned Liodillo loudly roared,
    And the Peccarbok whistled its whine,
The Chinchayak leapt on the dewy sward,
    As it hunted the pale Baboopine.

He dreamt that he met the Crocoghau,
    As it swam in the Stagnolent Lake;
But everything that in dreams he saw
    Came of eating too freely of cake.

Thomas Hood

The Vulture

The vulture eats between his meals,
   And that's the reason why
He very, very rarely feels
   As well as you and I.
His eye is dull, his head is bald,
   His neck is growing thinner.
Oh! What a lesson for us all
   To only eat at dinner!

Hilaire Belloc

20th

Birds of a Feather will Flock Together

Birds of a feather will flock together
And so will pigs and swine.
Rats and mice will have their choice
And so will I have mine.

Anon.

Bessie By Day

This here
dirt just
gotta go,

Bessie frown
and Bessie know.
Put a
kerchief
on her head,

Beat that dirt
until it dead.

That much
better,
Bessie say

as she smile
and walk away.

Myra Cohn Livingston

22**nd**

Beside the Line of Elephants

I think they had no pattern
When they cut out the elephant's skin;
Some places it need letting out,
And others, taking in.

Edna Becker

Rules For Cooking Toast

Be accurate when cooking toast
Never try to guess
Cook it 'til it smokes and then
Twenty seconds less.

Anon.

The Mitten Song

"Thumbs in the thumb-place,
fingers all together!"
This is the song
We sing in mitten-weather,
When it is cold, it doesn't matter whether
Mittens are wool,
Or made of finest leather –
This is the song
We sing in mitten-weather:
"Thumbs in the thumb-place,
Fingers all together!"

Marie Louise Allen

I Passed by his Garden

I passed by his garden, and marked, with one eye,
How the Owl and the Panther were sharing a pie:
The panther took pie-crust, and gravy, and meat,
While the Owl had the dish as its share of the
  treat.

When the pie was all finished, the Owl, as a boon,
Was kindly permitted to pocket the spoon:
While the Panther received knife and fork with a
  growl
And concluded the banquet by –

Lewis Carroll

26th

from Night

The sun descending in the west
The evening star does shine,
The birds are silent in their nest
And I must seek for mine,
The moon, like a flower
In heaven's high bower,
With silent delight
Sits and smiles on the night.

William Blake

27th

At Night

When night is dark
my cat is wise
to light the lanterns
in his eyes

Aileen Fisher

A Wolf

A wolf
I considered myself
but
the owls are hooting
and
the night I fear.

Traditional,
Osage Indian

The Poet

The morning sky was flocked with words
Flying high like singing birds
He fed them breath and light and bread
And now they're on this page instead.

Gareth Owen

Somewhere in the Sky

Somewhere
In the sky,
There's a door painted blue,
With a big brass knocker seven feet high.
If you can find it,
Knock, and go through –
That is, if you dare.
You'll see behind it
The secrets of the universe piled on a chair
Like a tangle of wool.
A voice will declare,
"You have seven centuries in which to unwind it.

But whatever
You do,
You must never,
Ever,
Lose your temper and pull."

Leo Aylen

December

1st

Hannukah

Light the candles
Me and you
One, two

Pray for peace
Evermore
Three, four

Hold hands
Hug and kiss
Five, six

Always love
Never hate
Seven, eight.

Andrea Shavick

The Park

I'm glad that I live near a park
for in winter, after dark,
The park lights shine,
As bright and still as dandelions
on a hill.

Rochelle Beman, age 11

3rd

Go to Bed, Tom

Go to bed, Tom,
Go to bed, Tom,
Tired or not, Tom,
Go to bed, Tom.

Anon.

Dog

Asleep he wheezes at his ease.
He only wakes to scratch his fleas.

He hogs the fire, he bakes his head
As if it were a loaf of bread.

He's just a sack of snoring dog.
You can lug him like a log.

You can roll him with your foot.
He'll stay snoring where he's put.

Take him out for exercise
He'll roll in cowclap up to his eyes.

He will not race, he will not romp.
He saves his strength for gobble and chomp.

He'll work as hard as you could wish
Emptying the dinner dish.

Then flops flat, and digs down deep,
Like a miner, into sleep.

Ted Hughes

5th

I Heard a Bird Sing

I heard a bird sing
In the dark of December
A magical thing
And sweet to remember.

"We are nearer to spring
Than we were in September,"
I heard a bird sing
In the dark of December.

Oliver Herford

There was a King . . .

There was a king, and he had three daughters,
And they all lived in a basin of water;
    The basin bended –
    My story's ended.
If the basin had been stronger,
My story would have been longer.

Anon.

7th

Fruit Jokes

The satsuma
Has no sense of
Humour
But a fig'll
Giggle

Adrian Mitchell

Learner

Oh, Matilda, look at your uncle Jim,
He's in the bathtub learning how to swim.
First he does the front stroke, then he does
   the side,
Now he's underwater swimming against
   the tide.

Anon.

Haiku: winter downpour

Winter downpour –
even the monkey
needs a raincoat.

Basho
(Translated by Lucien Stryk)

Gaelic Blessing

Deep peace of the running wave to you.
Deep peace of the flowing air to you.
Deep peace of the quiet air to you.
Deep peace of the shining stars to you.
Deep peace of the Son of Peace to you.

Anon.

from The Earthly Paradise

Folk say, a wizard to a northern king
At Christmas-tide such wondrous things did show,
That through one window men beheld the spring,
And through another saw the summer glow,
And through a third the fruited vines a-row
While still, unheard, but in its wonted way,
Piped the drear wind of that December day.

William Morris

The Garden Year

January brings the snow,
Makes our feet and fingers glow.

February brings the rain,
Thaws the frozen lake again.

March brings breezes loud and shrill,
Stirs the dancing daffodil.

April brings the primrose sweet,
Scatters daisies at our feet.

May brings flocks of pretty lambs,
Skipping by their fleecy dams.

June brings tulips, lilies, roses,
Fills the children's hands with posies.

December

Hot July brings cooling showers,
Apricots and gillyflowers.

August brings the sheaves of corn,
Then the harvest home is borne.

Warm September brings the fruit,
Sportsmen then begin to shoot.

Fresh October brings the pheasant,
Then to gather nuts is pleasant.

Dull November brings the blast,
Then the leaves are whirling fast.

Chill December brings the sleet,
Blazing fire, and Christmas treat.

Sara Coleridge

Little Robin Redbreast

Little Robin Redbreast
Sat upon a tree,
He sang merrily,
As merrily as could be.
He nodded with his head,
And his tail waggled he,
As little Robin Redbreast
Sat upon a tree.

Anon.

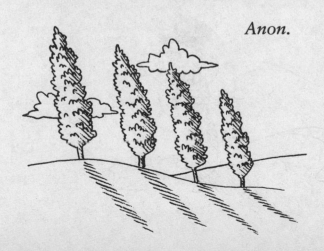

Snow

Out of the bosom of the air,
Out of the cloudfolds of her garment shaken,
Over the woodlands, brown and bare,
Over the harvest-fields forsaken,
Silent, and soft, and slow
Descends the snow.

Henry Wadsworth Longfellow

Secret Door

The upstairs room
has a secret door.
Dad says someone
used it for
some papers many years ago,
and if I want to, I can go
and bring a treasured thing
to hide and lock it up
all dark inside

and it can be
a place for me
to open
with
its
tiny
key.

Myra Cohn Livingston

Winter Moon

How thin and sharp is the moon tonight!
How thin and sharp and ghostly white
Is the slim curved crook of the moon tonight!

Langston Hughes

Night-lights

There is no need to light a night-light
On a light night like tonight;
For a night-light's light's a slight light
When the moonlight's white and bright.

Anon.

Nativity

Oh Miss, I don't want to be Joseph,
Miss, I really don't want to be him,
With a cloak of bright red and a towel on my head
And a cotton wool beard on my chin.

Oh Miss, please don't make me a shepherd.
I just won't be able to sleep.
I'll go weak at the knees and wool makes me
   sneeze
And I really am frightened of sheep.

Oh Miss, I just can't be the landlord,
Who says there's no room in the inn.
I'll get in a fright when it comes to the night
And I know that I'll let Mary in.

Oh Miss, you're not serious – an angel?
Can't Peter take that part instead?
I'll look such a clown in a white silky gown,
And a halo stuck up on me head.

Oh Miss, I am not being a camel!
Or cow or an ox or an ass!
I'll look quite absurd and I won't say a word,
And all of the audience will laugh.

Oh Miss, I'd rather not be a Wise Man,
Who brings precious gifts from afar.
But the part right for me, and I hope you'll agree,
In this play – can I be the star?

Gervase Phinn

Snap

Thanks for the photo
It really was nice
I put it in the attic
To scare away the mice.

Anon.

The Christmas Pudding

Into the basin
put the plums,
Stir-about, stir-about,
 stir-about!

Next the good
white flour comes,
Stir about, stir-about,
 stir-about!

Sugar and peel
and eggs and spice,
Stir-about, stir-about,
 stir-about!

Mix them and fix them
and cook them twice,
Stir-about, stir-about,
    stir-about!

Anon.

Custard

I like it thin without a skin,
My sister likes it thicker.
But thick or thin, when tucking in,
I'm noisier and quicker.

Colin West

22nd

Bells

We went to a party
On Christmas Eve
And after tea
Mrs Turney said SSSSSSSSSHHHHHHH
So we sssssssshed
And we heard them
The jingle of bells
The reindeer wear
Because they don't have hooters

Hiawyn Oram

At Nine of the Night I Opened My Door

At nine of the night I opened my door
That stands midway between moor and moor,
And all around me, silver-bright,
I saw that the world had turned to white.

Thick was the snow on field and hedge
And vanished was the river-sedge,
Where winter skilfully had wound
A shining scarf without a sound.

And as I stood and gazed my fill
A stable-boy came down the hill.
With every step I saw him take
Flew at his heel a puff of flakc.

December

His brow was whiter than the hoar,
A beard of freshest snow he wore,
And round about him, snowflake starred,
A red horse-blanket from the yard.

In a red cloak I saw him go,
His back was bent, his step was slow,
And as he laboured through the cold
He seemed a hundred winters old.

I stood and watched the snowy head,
The whiskers white, the cloak of red.
"A merry Christmas!" I heard him cry.
"The same to you, old friend," said I.

Charles Causley

Carol

Villagers all, this frosty tide,
Let your doors swing open wide,
Through wind may follow, and snow beside,
Yet draw us in by your fire to bide;
 Joy shall be yours in the morning!

Here we stand in the cold and the sleet,
Blowing fingers and stamping feet,
Come from far away you to greet –
You by fire and we in the street –
 Bidding you joy in the morning!

For ere one half of the night was gone,
Sudden a star has led us on,
Raining bliss and benison –
Bliss tomorrow and more anon,
 Joy for every morning!

Goodman Joseph toiled through the snow –
Saw the star o'er a stable low;
Mary she might not further go –
Welcome thatch, and litter below!
  Joy was hers in the morning!

And then they heard the angels tell
"Who were the first to cry Nowell?
Animals all, as it befell,
In the stable where they did dwell!
  Joy shall be theirs in the morning!"

Kenneth Grahame

25th

As I sat on a Sunny Bank

As I sat on a sunny bank
On Christmas day in the morning,
I saw three ships come sailing by
On Christmas day in the morning.
And who do you think were in those ships
But Joseph and his fair lady;
He did whistle and she did sing,
And all the bells on earth did ring
For joy our Saviour he was born
On Christmas day in the morning.

Anon.

Reindeer Report

Chimneys: colder.
Flightpaths: busier.
Driver: Christmas (F)
Still baffled by postcodes.

Children: more
And stay up later.
Presents: heavier.
Pay: Frozen.

Mission in spite
Of all this
Accomplished.

U. A. Fanthorpe

Skating

When I try to skate,
My feet are so wary
They grit and grate;
And then I watch Mary
Easily gliding,
Like an ice-fairy;
Skimming and curving,
Out and in,
With a turn of her head,
And a twirl and a spin;
Sailing under
The breathless hush
Of the willows, and back
To the frozen rush;
Out to the island
And round the edge,

December

Skirting the rim
Of the crackling sedge,
Swerving close
To the poplar root,
And round the lake
On a single foot,
With a three, and an eight,
And a loop and a ring;
Where Mary glides,
The lake will sing!
Out in the mist
I hear her now
Under the frost
Of the willow-bough
Easily sailing,
Light and fleet
With the song of the lake
Beneath her feet.

Herbert Asquith

28th

The Last Dragon

By a dusk-damp cave
As the first snows fall
A dragon breathes;
The last of them all.

His eyes are dull,
His memories old;
His breath is pale,
His fire now cold.

The forest mice
Who ran from his roar
Now nest by his feet,
Afraid no more.

December

He turns his face
To the winter moon;
His claws are furled,
His courage gone.

The first owl swoops
To the forest floor;
But the last of the dragons
Is no more.

Judith Nicholls

The Great Land

In the future we will see
The great land all green and grassy,
Lots of animals with gleaming eyes,
Fantastic food full of colour,
Salad-green clothes, soft and clean,
A fantastic school with entertaining lessons.

Thomas Buchanan-Smith, age 6

30th

Benediction

Thanks to the ear
that someone may hear

Thanks to seeing
that someone may see

Thanks to feeling
that someone may feel

Thanks to touch
that one may be touched

Thanks to flowering of white moon
And spreading shawl of black night
Holding villages and cities together.

James Berry

Cat's Note

How often can you take a poem
And stroke it in your lap?

John Agard

Index of first lines

Index of poets

Index of poets

Acknowledgements

The publishers wish to thank the following for permission to use copyright material:

John Agard, 'Cats' Note' and 'Bedbugs' from *We Animals Would Like a Word With You* by John Agard, Bodley Head (1996), by permission of Caroline Sheldon Literary Agency on behalf of the author; and 'The Older the Violin the Sweeter the Tune' from *Say It Again, Granny!* by John Agard, Bodley Head, by permission of the Random House Group Ltd; **Allan Ahlberg**, 'I See a Seagull' from *Heard it in the Playground* by Allan Ahlberg, Viking (1989). Copyright © Allan Ahlberg, 1989, by permission of Penguin Group Ltd; **Jez Alborough**, 'Running' from *Shake Before Opening* by Jez Alborough, Hutchinson (1991), by permission of The Random House Group Ltd; **Dorothy Aldis**, 'Singing' from *Everything and Anything* by Dorothy Aldis. Copyright © 1925–27, renewed 1953, © 1954, 1955 by Dorothy Aldis; and 'The Picnic' from *All Together* by Dorothy Aldis. Copyright © 1926–28, 1934, 1939, 1952, renewed 1953, © 1954–56, 1962 by Dorothy Aldis, © 1967 by Roy E. Porter, renewed, by permission of G. P. Putnam's Sons, an imprint of Penguin Putnam Books for Young Readers, a division of Penguin Putnam Inc; **Marie Louise Allen**, 'The Mitten Song' from *A Pocketful of Poems* by Marie Louise Allen. Copyright © 1957 by Marie Allen Howarth, by permission of HarperCollins*Publishers*, Inc; **Moira Andrew**, 'Lion King', first published in *Wacky Wild Animals*, ed. Brian Moses, Macmillan Education (2000), by permission of the author; **Herbert Asquith**, 'Skating'. Copyright © Michael Asquith and Vivien Asquith, by permission of Michael Asquith; **Kelly Bambrick**, 'Emma and Rebecca' from *Cadbury's Ninth Book of Children's Poetry* (1991), by permission of Cadbury Schweppes; **Hilaire Belloc**, 'The Vulture' from *Complete Verse* by Hilaire Belloc, Random House. Copyright © The Estate of Hilaire Belloc, 1970, by permission of The Peters Fraser and Dunlop Group Ltd on behalf of the Estate of the author; **Rachelle Beman**, 'The Park' from *Hey Mister Butterfly* (1978) ILEA, by permission of English and Media Centre; **Gerard Benson**, 'Fishing' from *Evidence of Elephants*, Viking (1995) and 'Molligan's Rock' from *The Magnificent Callisto*, Blackie, (1992), by permission of the author; **James Berry**, 'Benediction' and 'One' from *The Ring of*

438

Acknowledgements

Words by James Berry, Hamish Hamilton. Copyright © James Berry, by permission of The Peters Fraser and Dunlop Group Ltd on behalf of the author; **Valerie Bloom**, 'Eat Your Veg' from *The World is Sweet*, Bloomsbury Children's Books (2000), by permission of the author; **Steve Bowkett**, 'Just Doing', by permission of the author; **Paul Bright**, 'Me and the ball and the wall', by permission of the author; **Margaret Wise Brown**, 'Little Donkey Close your Eyes' and 'The Secret Song' from *Nibble, Nibble* by Margaret Wise Brown. Copyright © 1959 by William R. Scott, Inc, renewed 1987 by Roberta Brown Rauch, by permission of HarperCollins*Publishers*, Inc; **Jon Burnby**, 'Zebra' from *Hey Mister Butterfly* (1978) ILEA, by permission of English and Media Centre; **Caroline Byrne**, 'My granny's garden' from *Cadbury's Ninth Book of Children's Poetry* (1991), by permission of Cadbury Schweppes; **Charles Causley**, 'At Nine of the Night I Opened My Door' and 'Johnny Come Over the Water' from *Collected Poems for Children* by Charles Causley, Macmillan (1996), by permission of David Higham Associates on behalf of the author; **G. K. Chesterton**, 'Triolet', by permission of A. P. Watt on behalf of the Royal Literary Fund; **Elizabeth Coatsworth**, 'The Mouse' from *Compass Rose* by Elizabeth Coatsworth. Copyright © 1929 by Coward-McCann, Inc, renewed © 1957 by Elizabeth Coatsworth, by permission of Coward-McCann, an imprint of Penguin Putnam Books for Young Readers, a division of Penguin Putnam Inc; **Wendy Cope**, 'My Old Guitar' from *Twiddling Your Thumbs* by Wendy Cope, Faber. Copyright © Wendy Cope by permission of The Peters Fraser and Dunlop Group Ltd on behalf of the author; **Frances Cornford**, 'Dogs', by permission of the Trustees of the author's Estate, James Peter Cornford and William John Bellamy; **E. E. Cummings**, 'who are you, little i' from *Complete Poems 1904–1962* by E. E. Cummings, ed. George J. Firmage. Copyright © 1991, by the trustees for the E. E. Cummings Trust and George James Firmage, by permission of W. W. Norton & Company; **Emily Dickinson**, 'Bee! I'm expecting you', 'A word is dead' and 'I'm Nobody! Who are You' from *The Poems of Emily Dickinson*, ed. Thomas H. Johnson, The Belknap Press of Harvard University Press. Copyright © 1951, 1955, 1979, by the President and Fellows of Harvard College, by permission of the publishers and the Trustees of Amherst College; **Peter Dixon**, 'Cat March', 'Moving Away' and 'Before the Days of Noah' from *The Penguin in the Fridge* by Peter Dixon (2000), by permission of the author; **Helen Dunmore**, 'Baby Orang-utan', 'Lemon Sole' and 'Night Cat' from *Secrets* by Helen Dunmore, Bodley Head, by permission of A.

439

Acknowledgements

P. Watt Ltd on behalf of the author; **Richard Edwards**, 'Joe Bright', 'Shaggy Dogs' and 'When I was Three' from *Teaching the Parrot* by Richard Edwards, Faber and Faber, by permission of the author; and 'Round and Round' from *Whispers from a Wardrobe* by Richard Edwards, Lutterworth Press (1987), by permission of Lutterworth Press; **U. A. Fanthorpe**, 'Reindeer Reports' from *Standing To* by U. A. Fanthorpe (1982). Copyright © 1982 U. A. Fanthorpe, by permission of Peterloo Poets; **Eleanor Farjeon**, 'Waking Up', 'Bedtime' and 'The Night Will Never Stay' from *Blackbird Has Spoken* by Eleanor Farjeon, Macmillan, by permission of David Higham Associates on behalf of the Estate of the author; **Aileen Fisher**, 'At Night' and 'In the Sun and Shadow' from *Out in the Dark and Daylight* by Aileen Fisher. Copyright (1980) by Aileen Fisher, by permission of Marian Reiner on behalf of the author; **Vivian French**, 'A Fishy Thought' from *The Big Book of Little Poems*, Andre Deutsch (1999), by permission of the author; **Roy Fuller**, 'End of a Girl's First Tooth' from *The World Through the Window*, Blackie Children's Books (1989), by permission of John Fuller; **Carmen de Gasztold**, 'The Prayer of the Butterfly' and 'The Prayer of the Ox' from *Prayers from the Ark*, translated by Rumer Godden, 1963, by permission of Macmillan Children's Books; **Pamela Gillilan**, 'First Fox' included in *Another Second Poetry Book*, Oxford University Press, by permission of the author; **Nikki Giovanni**, 'one of the problems of play' from *Spin a Soft Black Song*, revised edition, by Nikki Giovanni. Copyright © 1971, 1985 by Nikki Giovanni, by permission of Farrar Straus and Giroux LLC; **Antonia Goldfinger**, 'I Hope' from *Hey Mister Butterfly* (1978) ILEA, by permission of English and Media Centre; **Virginia Graham**, 'October Boy', by permission of the Estate of the author; **Robert Graves**, 'Henry and Mary' from *Complete Poems by Robert Graves*, by permission of Carcanet Press Ltd; **Emma Gregory**, 'Hedgehog' from *Cadbury's Ninth Book of Children's Poetry* (1991), by permission of Cadbury Schweppes; **Ranjeet Mohan Guptara**, 'The Literary Cat', first published in *Can I Buy a Slice of Sky*, ed. Grace Nichols, Blackie and Sons (1991), by permission of the author; **Anne Harvey**, 'Totteridge Fields' from *Occasions*, selected by Anne Harvey, Blackie (1990). Copyright © Anne Harvey 1990, by permission of Penguin Books Ltd; **John Hegley**, 'A Three Legged Friend' from *These Were Your Fathers* by John Hegley, Kingfisher. Copyright © John Hegley by permission of Peters Fraser and Dunlop Group Ltd on behalf of the author; **Florence Parry Heide**, 'What You Don't Know About Food' from *Grim and Ghastly Goings-*

On, originally published by Lothrop, Lee and Shepard Books. Copyright © Diana Hendry 1995, by permission of Curtis Brown, Ltd on behalf of the author; **Langston Hughes**, 'Winter Moon' from *The Collected Poems of Langston Hughes* by Langston Hughes. Copyright © 1994 by The Estate of Langston Hughes, by permission of David Higham Associates on behalf of the author and Alfred A. Knopf, a division of Random House, Inc; **Ted Hughes**, 'Dog' from *What is the Truth?* by Ted Hughes, by permission of Faber and Faber Ltd; **Kobayashi Issa**, 'Haiku' from *The Autumn Wind*, translated by Lewis Mackenzie, by permission of John Murray (Publishers) Ltd; **Elizabeth Jennings**, 'Rhyme for Children' from *A Spell of Words* by Elizabeth Jennings, Macmillan, by permission of David Higham Associates on behalf of the author; **Jenny Joseph**, 'Getting Back Home', by permission of John Johnson Ltd on behalf of the author; **Jackie Kay**, 'The Frog Who Dreamed She Was an Opera Singer' from *The Frog Who Dreamed She Was an Opera Singer* by Jackie Kay (1998), by permisssion of Bloomsbury Publishing; **Rudyard Kipling**, 'The White Seal's Lullaby', by permission of A. P. Watt Ltd on behalf of *The National Trust for Places of Historic Interest of Natural Beauty*; **Dennis Lee**, 'The Coat' from *The Difficulty of Living on Other Planets*, Macmillan of Canada (1987). Copyright © Dennis Lee, by permission of Westwood Creative Artists on behalf of the author; **Jean Little**, 'Pearls' from *Hey World, Here I Am!* by Jean Little. Copyright © 1986 by Jean Little, by permission of Kids Can Press Ltd, Toronto, and HarperCollins*Publishers*, Inc; **Myra Cohn Livingston**, 'Bessie by Day' from *No Way of Knowing Dallas Poems* by Myra Cohn Livingston. Copyright © 1980 by Myra Cohn Livingston, by permission of Marian Reiner on behalf of the author; and 'Secret Door' from *Worlds I Know and Other Poems* by Myra Cohn Livingston. Copyright © 1985 by Myra Cohn Livingston, by permission of Margaret K. McElderry Books, an imprint of Simon and Schuster Children's Publishing Division; **Amy Lowell**, 'The Fisherman's Wife' from *The Complete Poetical Works of Amy Lowell*. Copyright © 1955 by Houghton Mifflin Company, renewed © 1983 by Houghton Mifflin Company, Brinton P. Roberts and G. D'Andelot Belin, Esq., by permission of Houghton Mifflin Company; **David McCord**, 'Every Time I Climb A Tree' and 'This is My Rock' from *Far and Few* by David McCord. Copyright © 1952 by David McCord, by permission of Little, Brown and Company, Inc; **Roger McGough**, 'A Poem with Knickers in It' from *Nailing the Shadow* by Roger McGough, Puffin (1987), 'Sneezes' from *Pillow Talk* by Roger McGough, Viking (1990). Copyright © Roger McGough, by permission of Peters Fraser and Dunlop Group Ltd on behalf of the author; **Ian McMillan**, 'An Interesting Fact About One of my Relatives', 'Batman's Exercise Video', 'New Day', 'The Fog and Me' and 'Elephant Dream' from *The Very Best of Ian McMillan* by Ian McMillan, Macmillan (2001), by permission of the author; **Lindsay MacRae**, 'Animal Rights' from *Yer Canny Shove Yer Granny Off a Bus!* Copyright © 1995 by Lindsay MacRae, Viking, by permission of The Agency (London) Ltd on behalf of the author; **Wes Magee,** 'The Bestest Bear Song'. Copyright © Wes Magee, by permission of the author; **Margaret Mahy**, 'Sensible Questions' from *Nonstop Nonsense* by Margaret Mahy, J. M. Dent Children's Books, by permission of Orion Publishing Group Ltd; **Gerda Mayer**, 'May Poem' first published in *Expression*, 1967 and 'Bilberries' by the permission of the author; **Eve Merriam**, 'Weather' and 'Catch a Little Rhyme' from *Jamboree: Rhymes for All Times* by Eve Merriam. Copyright © 1962, 1964, 1966, 1973, 1984 by Eve Merriam, by permission of Marian Reiner on behalf of the author; **Spike Milligan,** 'Granny' from *Silly Verse for Kids and Animals* by Spike Milligan (1984) and 'Rain' from *A Children's Treasury* by Spike Milligan, Virgin (1999), by permission of Spike Milligan Productions Ltd; **Trevor Millum**, 'Dick's Dog'. Copyright © Trevor Millum, by permission of the author; **Adrian Mitchell**, 'A Cat Called Slumber' and 'Fruit Jokes' from *Balloon Lagoon and The Magic Islands of Poetry* by Adrian Mitchell, Orchard Books (1997). Copyright © Adrian Mitchell, by permission of Peters Fraser and Dunlop Group Ltd on behalf of the author; **Tony Mitton**, 'Dreaming the Unicorn' from *Plum* by Tony Mitton, Scholastic Children's Books (1998), 'Spider' from *The Red and White Spotted Handkerchief* by Tony Mitton, Scholastic Children's Books (2000), and 'Penny Piece' from *The Horrible Headmonster*, Macmillan (2001), by permission of David Higham Associates on behalf of the author; **Lilian Moore**, 'New Sounds' from *Little Raccoon and Poems from the Woods* by Lilian Moore. Copyright © 1975 by Lilian Moore; and 'Until I Saw the Sea' from *I Feel the Same Way* by Lilian Moore. Copyright © 1967, 1995 by Lilian Moore, by permission of Marian Reiner on behalf of the author; **Jeffrey Moss**, 'The Monster' and 'Dad and Me' from *The Butterfly Jar* by Jeff Moss. Copyright © 1989 by Jeff Moss, by permission of Bantam Books, a division of Random House, Inc and International Creative Management, Inc on behalf of the author; **Ogden Nash**, 'The Mules' from *Candy Is Dandy: The Best of Ogden Nash*. Copyright © 1953 by

Acknowledgements

Ogden Nash, renewed, by permission of Curtis Brown, Ltd on behalf of the author and Andre Deutsch Ltd; **Judith Nicholls**, 'Last Dragon' from *Storm's Eye* by Judith Nicholls, Oxford University Press. Copyright © 1994 Judith Nicholls, by permission of the author; and 'Who's There' from *Midnight Forest* by Judith Nicholls (1987), by permission of Faber and Faber Ltd; **Grace Nichols**, 'Crab Dance' and 'My Cousin Melda' from *Come Into My Tropical Garden* by Grace Nichols. Copyright © Grace Nichols 1988, by permission of Curtis Brown Ltd, London, on behalf of the author; **Hiawyn Oram**, 'Bells' from *Speaking for Ourselves* by Hiawyn Oram, Methuen. Copyright © Hiawyn Oram 1990, by permission of Rogers, Coleridge & White Ltd on behalf of the author; **Jack Ousbey**, 'Fruit Picking', first published in *The Works*, chosen by Paul Cookson, Macmillan (2000), by permission of the author; **Gareth Owen**, 'The Owl and the Astronaut' from *Collected Poems for Children*, Macmillan Children's Books. Copyright © Gareth Owen 2000; and 'Jack in the Sky' and 'The Book', by permission of Rogers, Coleridge & White on behalf of the author; **Brian Patten**, 'The Tree and the Pool' and 'The Whale's Hymn' from *Gargling with Jelly*, Viking (1985). Copyright © Brian Patten 1985, by permission of Penguin Books Ltd and Rogers, Coleridge & White Ltd on behalf of the author; **Andrew Fusek Peters**, 'Short Poem', by permission of the author; **Jack Prelutsky**, 'They Never Send Sam to the Store Anymore' and 'My Sister Ate an Orange' from *Something BIG Has Been Here* by Jack Prelutsky. Copyright © 1990 by Jack Prelutsky, by permission of HarperCollins*Publishers*, Inc; **James Reeves**, 'Fireworks' from *Complete Poems for Children by James Reeves*, Heinemann, by permission of Laura Cecil Literary Agency on behalf of the author; **E. V. Rieu**, 'The Hippopotamus's Birthday', by permission of Authors' Licensing & Collection Society on behalf of the Estate of the author; **Michael Rosen**, 'I'm Just Going Out for a Moment' from *Wouldn't You Like to Know* by Michael Rosen, Andre Deutsch (1997). Copyright © Michael Rosen, by permission of Peters Fraser and Dunlop Group Ltd on behalf of the author; **Coral Rumble**, 'Egg', first published in *Fireworks*, ed. John Foster, Oxford University Press (2000), by permission of the author; **Vita Sackville-West**, 'Full Moon'. Copyright (c) The Estate of Vita Sackville-West, by permission of Curtis Brown Group Ltd, London on behalf of the Estate of the author; **Carl Sandburg**, 'Fog' from *Chicago Poems* by Carl Sandburg. Copyright (c) 1916 by Holt, Rinehart and Winston, renewed © 1944 by Carl Sandburg, by permission of Harcourt, Inc; **Shel Silverstein**, 'The Farmer and the Queen' from *Where the Sidewalk Ends* by Shel Silverstein. Copyright © 1974 by Evil Eye Music, Inc, by permission of HarperCollins*Publishers*, Inc and Edite Kroll Literary Agency, Inc, on behalf of the author; **Matt Simpson**, 'Rosie's Are Red', by permission of the author; **Ian Souter**, 'You Don't Frighten Me!'. Copyright © Ian Souter, by permission of the author; **Steve Turner**, 'It Wasn't Me' and 'Words I Like' from *The Day I Fell Down the Toilet* by Steve Turner, by permission of Lion Publishing; **Celia Warren**, 'Penguins on Ice', first published in *Wacky Wild Animals*, ed. Brian Moses, Macmillan (2000), by permission of the author; **Clive Webster**, 'Jungle Wedding', by permission of the author; **Zaro Weil**, 'Wake Up' from *Mud Moon and Me* by Zaro Weil, Orchard Books (1989), by permission of The Watts Publishing Group Ltd; **Colin West**, 'Custard' and 'Me and Amanda', by permission of the author; **Valerie Worth**, 'Caterpillar' from *All the Small Poems and Fourteen More* by Valerie Worth. Copyright © 1987, 1994 by Valerie Worth, by permission of Farrar, Straus and Giroux, LLC; **Kit Wright**, 'Red Boots On' from *Poems 1974–1983* by Kit Wright, Random Century Ltd, by permission of the author; **Samuel Yardley**, 'Fireworks' from *Cadbury's Ninth Book of Children's Poetry* (1991), by permission of Cadbury Schweppes; **Yayu**, 'Haiku' from *Birds, Frogs, and Moonlight*, translated by Sylvia Cassedy and Kunihiro Suetake. Copyright © 1967 by Doubleday & Co., by permission of Ellen Cassedy; **Benjamin Zephaniah**, 'Jamaican Summers' from *Wicked World* by Benjamin Zephaniah, Puffin (2000). Copyright © Benjamin Zephaniah, 2000, by permission of Penguin Group Ltd; **Charlotte Zolotow**, 'Azalea' from *River Winding* by Charlotte Zolotow. Copyright © 1970 by Charlotte Zolotow, by permission of Scott Treimel, NY on behalf of the author.

Every effort has been made to trace the copyright holders but we have been unable to trace a number of poets, or their heirs. The publishers will be glad to hear from any such copyright holders.